# THE TOPOGRAPHY OF
# STANE STREET

# THE TOPOGRAPHY
# OF STANE STREET

*A critical Review of " The Stane Street "
by Hilaire Belloc*

By

## CAPTAIN W. A. GRANT
LATE 13TH HUSSARS

*WITH FOUR DIAGRAMS AND A MAP*

LONDON
## JOHN LONG LIMITED
NORRIS STREET, HAYMARKET
MCMXXII

## TO
## PITTI-SING

" Her taste exact
  For faultless fact
  Amounts to a disease."
                    *The Mikado*

# CONTENTS

7

# The Topography of Stane Street

## INTRODUCTORY

HAVING lived in West Sussex for a number of years, and frequently shot over those parts of the Goodwood, Eartham, Slindon, and Dale Park estates on which are to be found the best preserved and most conspicuous portions of the Stane Street, the existence of this ancient Roman way was, of course, well known to me—a familiarity which may perhaps have bred some measure of contempt, since hitherto I had given to it no more than the passing interest aroused by so visible a connecting link between ancient and modern times.

Although published in 1913, it was not until quite recently, and by the merest accident, that the work under review [1] came into my hands. The author has evidently devoted to his subject many hours of study, and of historical and archæological research, and on these branches of the subject I do not pretend to offer an opinion, my criticism being confined to the topographical work only, and the conclusions deduced therefrom.

I should imagine that topographical surveying, and the principles upon which maps are constructed, is a subject on which few people outside the Staff of the

[1] *The Stane Street*, by Hilaire Belloc.

Ordnance Survey or The Royal Engineers, have anything beyond a superficial and elementary knowledge. Perhaps that is the reason why no previous writer has, so far as I know, attempted to deal with the subject on accurate topographical lines. But Mr. Belloc has not hesitated to rush in where others have feared to tread, with results that merely tend to emphasise the wisdom of those others in leaving it alone.

Mr. Belloc is obviously an adept in the matter of map reading. But map reading and map making are two very different things, and it is evident from the conclusions he arrives at, and from some of his remarks which I will deal with in due course, that the topographical section of the work has been undertaken with an insufficient knowledge of the subject. Also the work, such as it is, has been executed with a degree of carelessness and inaccuracy that is almost incredible. Quite apart from mathematical errors in computing angles, distances, or alignments, and from mis-statements arising therefrom (of which there are over ninety) the book contains no less than twenty-eight perfectly obvious mistakes due to sheer carelessness (or possibly printers' errors) which might, and ought to, have been corrected in revising the proofs. Particulars of these will be found in the Appendix. Also the folding map at the end of the book, and several of the sketch maps in the text, are incorrectly drawn, and are incompatible with each other and with the text they are designed to illustrate (see Appendix A and B).

I believe that *The Stane Street* ranks as a standard work and textbook on the subject, but it is unthinkable that such gross errors as this book contains should be allowed to pass unchallenged, and it is solely in the interests of historical and archæological truth that I have undertaken the task of correcting them.

Mr. Belloc has a very pleasant and convincing style of writing, and a way of surrounding his work with a mass of references, technical terms, and circumstantial detail in the form of " exact " measurements, heights, distances, bearings, diagrams, etc., which convey to the unsuspecting reader the impression that here, indeed, is a master of his subject whose utterances may be accepted without question. It was in this frame of mind that, having read Part I with newly aroused interest, I embarked upon Part II.

Part I deals with " Roman roads in Britain generally," and Part II with " The particular case of Stane Street."

A considerable experience of textbooks, together with a natural taste for exactitude on the printed page, has given me the habit of verifying statements in books so far as the means of doing so are available. Now it so happens that topographical surveying has always been a hobby of mine, and, in addition to Colonel Close's admirable textbook on the subject, I had in my possession the local sheets of the 6-inch Ordnance Map, and was therefore well equipped to accompany Mr. Belloc over the alignments of Stane Street.

Hitherto only one mistake had manifested itself, in the footnote on page 22, where the 2-inch Ordnance Map is referred to when obviously the $\frac{1}{2}$-inch map is meant. This I regarded as a mere printer's error which had escaped notice, and proceeded with Part II with unimpaired faith in the author. It soon became apparent, however, that in the matter of topography all these technical terms, bearings, distances, etc., were, in the words of " Pooh-Bah "—" merely corroborative details calculated to give an air of verisimilitude to a bald and unconvincing narrative " (I quote from memory).

But before entering upon the details of these alignments it may be well, for the information of those having no previous knowledge of the subject, to give a brief summary of what is already known about it.

The Stane Street, then, was the old Saxon name given to the Roman road which was built, for purely military purposes, with the object of connecting Chichester and London by the shortest possible route, having regard to the natural obstacles and difficulties to be met with, and to the military requirement of providing suitable sites for at least four permanent Camps, or *Mansiones* at intervals of one day's march. Naturally, the shortest possible route would have been a straight line. But this would have involved a double crossing of the South Downs, over very severe gradients, followed by a climb to over 700 feet over Holmbury Hill, which is a western spur of the Leith Hill group ; a descent to the 200-foot level, followed by a precipitous climb to Ranmore Common, unless a considerable divergence were made through Dorking Gap. For these reasons, the direct route was abandoned and a divergence made to the Eastward (Mr. Belloc says it is to the Westward, page 87) via Pulborough, by which, at a sacrifice of only 1 mile and 3 furlongs in point of distance, the following advantages were secured : A single passage of the South Downs over the easiest possible gradients ; better sites for the Camps at more convenient intervals ; and, from Pulborough onwards, a gently undulating route involving a divergence through Dorking Gap no greater than would have been necessary by the direct alignment from Chichester to London Bridge. There are reasons for supposing that the road was built, or at least planned, from London Bridge to Chichester, but for the purpose of this description I am following in Mr. Belloc's footsteps and taking it in the opposite direction.

Starting then from the Old East Gate of Chichester, the Stane Street takes a bee line for Hardham Camp near Pulborough, the terminus of the first day's march, in a direction N.E. ¾ E. For the first 5 miles, passing through Westhampnett and Halnaker, the ancient and modern roads practically coincide, except for two slight divergences. Here the modern road goes off to the left to Petworth, while the Stane Street keeps straight on through Eartham Wood and North Wood (the greater part of these have now been cut down to provide timber for War purposes), past Gumber Farm and thence by an easy slope to the summit of the South Downs at what is called " Gumber Corner," about 8¼ miles from Chichester.

This is one of the most interesting spots throughout the whole course of the road, for here it remains intact, just as the Romans left it nearly fifteen hundred years ago, and its construction, including the central "*vallum*," which was a feature of these Roman roads, can be followed without difficulty. Since the publication of Mr. Belloc's book, a very interesting paper on this subject has been contributed to the Sussex Archæological Society's collections by Mr. Eliot Curwen who made careful sections across the road with a view to discovering the methods of construction of the Roman engineers. But from the summit at Gumber Corner the road diverges first to the right and then to the left, so as to ease the very steep descent on the other side, and, on leaving the Down and getting onto cultivated land, nearly all traces of it have disappeared except at a few points where it can still be identified, and from which it appears that even after reaching the level at the base of the Downs, the alignment was not strictly adhered to, though for what reason does not transpire. The distance from Chichester to Hardham Camp is 13 miles, of which only the first five are still in use as a modern highway—part of the main road from Chichester to London via Petworth and Guildford.

Leaving Hardham Camp, the road follows very nearly the previous alignment for 1½ miles, to the crossing of the river Arun at the site of the present Pulborough Bridge. Here it begins to straighten up on its course towards London, pointing N.E. by N. for 2¾ miles to Todhurst Farm, where another slight bend to N.N.E. ½ E. occurs, and again at Billingshurst to N.N.E. ¼ E. From Billingshurst the Stane Street pursues an almost dead straight course for a distance of over 12 miles, passing through Five Oakes and Park Street to the second crossing of the Arun at Alfoldean Bridge, immediately south of which was the site of the second Camp, about 11½ miles from the first Camp at Hardham. The road continues past The Chequers, Rowhook (where another supposed Roman road branches off in a north-westerly direction), and through Ockley to Anstie Grange Farm, where it diverges to the left for the negociation of Dorking Gap. The conjectural site of the third Camp has been placed by Mr. Belloc, quite rightly, I think, in the middle of Dorking itself. From here the road crosses the river Mole at, or (according to Mr. Belloc) just to the west of the present Burford Bridge, and follows approximately the line of the modern road as far as Juniper Hill, where it bears to the right through Juniper Hill Wood, and, after skirting round a deep " Combe," emerges onto the summit of Mickleham Downs at what, for the purpose of this investigation, is called " point A," which will be more fully described later on. It is quite unmistakeable, whether looked for on the map or actually on the spot, and it is here that there begins that straight 2 miles of road, undoubtedly Roman, which has already been the subject of a good deal of controversy, and on which Mr. Belloc bases his final alignment on Old London Bridge. This piece of road points towards the site of Merton Abbey, but near Thirty Acres Barn it ceases to be straight, and gradually bends to the eastward until it points in the direction of the Grand Stand on Epsom Racecourse, near to which all trace of it is lost. Whether this piece of road is part of the Stane Street or not is more or less a matter of conjecture ; on the Ordnance Maps it is called " Ermyn Street," and no trace of a Roman road has been discovered between Thirty Acres Barn and Merton Abbey, a distance of 9 miles. The generally accepted theory appears to be that the Stane Street crossed the river Wandle at the site of the existing bridge near Merton Abbey ; that here, too, just south of the bridge, stood the fourth and last Camp, and from here the road followed a dead straight line to the crossing of the Thames at the site of Old London Bridge, 60 yards east of the modern bridge. Traces of the old Roman road have been found at various intermediate points which afford strong confirmation of this view ; but what seems to me the strongest argument of all, and one that Mr. Belloc's defective topography has entirely overlooked, is the fact that this last stretch of the road from Merton Abbey exactly coincides with the true alignment, or " great circle course " as it is called in navigation, from the East Gate of Chichester to Old London Bridge.

# MR. BELLOC'S ALIGNMENTS

> " This haughty youth,
> He speaks the truth,
> Whenever he finds it pays.
> And in this case
> It all took place
> Exactly as he says.
> Exactly—exactly—exactly,
> Ex—a—a—ctly as he says."
>
> *The Mikado*

" THE particular case of the Stane Street," which comprises " Part II " of Mr. Belloc's book begins at page 47, and on the very next page occasion arises for adverse criticism in the improper use of the word " trajectory," which he uses throughout the book to signify the " trace " or " lay-out " of the road. This is a term used chiefly in gunnery, and means the parabolic curve described by any body thrown, or projected, into the air.

Mr. Belloc's theory of the alignments, that is :

" The method by which the Stane Street was plotted out " (page 49), is that of :

" Four great limbs or sections each of which *can be directly proved* to have been planned from one point to another upon a straight line ! "

This is a very sweeping assertion, in support of which Mr. Belloc furnishes no proof whatever ; in fact, nothing in the nature of absolute proof seems possible, until such time as the researches of Antiquarians and Archæologists may bring to light further evidence. For the present we must be content with reasonable conjecture.

It is probably true that these alignments, whatever they may have been, were planned upon straight lines, because an alignment cannot be otherwise than straight, and that is the principle upon which the Roman roads were constructed ; but that they were either four in number, or followed the directions assigned to them by Mr. Belloc, are questions which I will now proceed to discuss.

The alleged

" four great limbs "

are as follows :

*First* from the East Gate of Chichester to the Southern end of Pulborough Bridge.

*Second* from a point near Pulborough called Borough Hill to a mark on the shoulder of Leith Hill called X or terminal D.

*Third* from the mark on the shoulder of Leith Hill to a mark called C on the shoulder of Juniper Hill.

*Fourth* from the mark C on Juniper Hill to the Southern end of Old London Bridge.

There is also a short subsidiary alignment from the Southern end of Pulborough Bridge to Todhurst Farm which cuts off the corner between the first and second alignments.

Mr. Belloc does not include in his scheme the direct alignment from Chichester to London Bridge ; in fact he rejects the idea of such an alignment having been plotted at all.

On page 63 he says :

" Had some such attempt been made to drive a road straight

from terminus to terminus. . . .  But no such one line has been even attempted."

And on page 57 he says :

" As a fact, the Roman road from Chichester to London does not follow this dead straight line from point to point.  Such a line would take it through Petworth Park (cutting the great pond there through its middle), and so going up through Abinger in Surrey (leaving Leith Hill well to the east) ; it would cut through the heart of Epsom just at the cross roads in the middle of that town.

So far as it goes this is perfectly true, and it would seem that, when it suits his purpose, Mr. Belloc can plot an alignment correctly enough.  But had he followed this alignment to its terminus at London Bridge he would have made a rather important discovery—that it also passes exactly through the site of Merton Abbey and the crossing of the Wandle, and that therefore the last stage of the road from Chichester, or the first stage out of London, coincides with that alignment.  On page 53 Mr. Belloc says :

" There is a common sense in history, although it is so rarely used."

Now it seems to me that in this case common sense would suggest that, before abandoning the point to point route, the Roman engineers would make a preliminary survey of the whole country involved, and not only plot out the direct alignment, but the alternative alignments via Pulborough as well ; they would also most likely fix, provisionally or approximately, the sites for their permanent Camps.  Moreover, in the absence of such preliminary survey, it is difficult to understand how they can have known in what direction to look for their alignments in the first instance.  I think, therefore, that we are justified in concluding that, not only was the direct alignment plotted out, but that it was a factor in the general scheme of the road.

On page 58 Mr. Belloc says :

"The straight line from the East Gate of Chichester to the southern end of London Bridge lies at an angle to the meridian 30° 25′ east of north,"

and on page 50 he says :

"The exact distance from one point to the other in a straight line is 55 miles and 3 furlongs."

Neither of these figures is correct. The true bearing from Chichester East Gate to Old London Bridge is 32° 30′ 27″·35, and the correct distance 291,144 feet = 55·1410 miles. In view of the fact that the alignment from Chichester appears to have been correctly plotted as far as Epsom, it is difficult to understand how Mr. Belloc's figures have been arrived at ; because, in order to plot an alignment correctly, it is necessary to know first of all the exact geographical position (i.e. the exact Latitude and Longitude) of the terminal points. From these the exact astronomical bearing or "Azimuth" must be computed, a complicated and tedious process, and from that again (another complicated and tedious process), the exact geographical position of any desired point on the alignment can be calculated, and plotted on the 6-inch Ordnance Map with a degree of accuracy equal to that of the map itself. Now an alignment from Chichester 30° 25′ East of North would pass about 2 miles to the west of Epsom, (*see* diagram Fig. 4, page 51) and, if produced to the distance of 55 miles and 3 furlongs, would arrive at a position about 40 yards south of University College, Gower Street, 2¼ miles north-west from Old London Bridge.

It may not be generally known that, owing to the

curvature of the earth's surface, and the impossibility of representing it with perfect accuracy on a flat sheet of paper, a straight line drawn on a map (except on the standard meridian, or due east or west on the equator) does not represent a corresponding straight alignment on the ground ; and conversely, a straight alignment on the ground takes the form of a slight curve when plotted on paper.  Over so short a distance as that from Chichester to London, the curvature is hardly appreciable on a map of small enough scale to cover the whole alignment, such as the $\frac{1}{4}$-inch Ordnance Map ; but when it comes to plotting it on successive sheets of the 6-inch map for the purpose of exact investigation, this curvature cannot be ignored, since in point of distance it amounts to some 400 yards, i.e. that is the maximum divergence of the true alignment from a straight line drawn on the map between Chichester and London Bridge.  The divergence of a " Mercator " or mean bearing course being about half that amount.

From what I can see of Mr. Belloc's work I do not think he knows how (or if he knows how he has not taken the trouble) to compute these bearings and alignments correctly, since throughout the whole book not a single bearing is correctly stated ; but what he appears to have done is this.  The $\frac{1}{4}$-inch Ordnance Map is divided into 2-inch squares which are lettered along one margin and numbered along the other for the purpose of indexing, so that the square containing any place required may be found at once.  Now if a straight line be drawn on this map from Chichester to London Bridge, and the angle of this line with regard to the lines of these squares be measured, the result will be found to agree so closely with the angle given by Mr. Belloc (30° 25′) as to afford reasonable probability that this was the method adopted. But the lines of these squares running more or less north and south are not meridians, nor are they parallel to any meridian within the limits of the map, so that the results attained are very wide of the mark, and quite useless for computing alignments, for which purpose the Azimuth must be calculated to one, or preferably two, places of decimals of a second of arc. And in any case, however correctly measured, such a method would only give the " Mercator " or " mean bearing," and not the Azimuth either from Chichester to London or from London to Chichester.

It may be well to explain here the difference between a " Bearing " and an " Azimuth," which is this : A " Bearing " is the angular direction of any point with regard to any other point whose position and Azimuth is known : usually, but not of necessity, the North Pole.

It is an ambiguous term which includes the following variations : An " observed " bearing, a " reduced " bearing, a " compass " bearing, a " true " bearing, an " initial " bearing, a " mean " bearing, a " final " bearing, a " reciprocal " bearing.

An " Azimuth," on the other hand, is an angular measurement which admits of no ambiguity. It is the true astronomical bearing (after making all corrections) of any point with regard to the Meridian at the point of observation, i.e. with regard to the sun at astronomical noon, which is true South. Azimuths are measured clockwise from South and Bearings from North, so that *true* Bearings and Azimuths are reciprocal. Both are expressed in degrees, minutes, and seconds of arc to two places of decimals from 0° to 360°, and not as Mr. Belloc expresses them, East of North in one case and North of East in another, which is very confusing and conducive to error.   This manner of expressing bearings was one of the first things that aroused my suspicions as to Mr. Belloc's topography, and led to this investigation.

Owing to the convergence of the meridians there is a difference of over half a degree between the " Azimuth " and " reverse Azimuth " (i.e. the Azimuths from Chichester to London and from London to Chichester respectively) so that a mean bearing could not in any case be within 15′ of that required for plotting the alignment.[1]

I propose now to take Mr. Belloc's " four great limbs " in detail.

[1] The " mean bearing " or " Mercator " course can easily be plotted on the map by dividing up the differences of Latitude and Longitude proportionally to the distance of any point required, but that is not the true alignment or " great circle " course.

# I

# From the East Gate of Chichester to the Southern End of Pulborough Bridge

O N page 87 Mr. Belloc says :

" The first limb was set straight from the East Gate of Chichester to Pulborough Bridge."

Page 213 :

" It is an alignment drawn *exactly* towards the crossing of the Arun at Pulborough Bridge,"

Page 228 :

" Taken along this summit at Gumber the road still points *exactly* to the Southern end of Pulborough Bridge."

It would be wearisome to quote all the repetitions of the above statement which occur throughout the book, but those given will serve to show the insistence with which Mr. Belloc harps upon the exactitude of the alignment upon Pulborough Bridge and the southern end of it. Why he should have gone out of his way to propound a fictitious alignment when the true alignment would have served his purpose equally well, it is difficult to understand. It seems to be the first of several instances where he fails to discriminate between the road itself and the alignment on which it is based, treating the two as interchangeable terms. Because the road crosses the Arun at Pulborough

Bridge he appears to have jumped to the conclusion that the alignment pointed there too, and adapted the facts to suit his arguments rather than deduce his arguments from the facts.

On page 65 he says :

" One has but to stand on the summit of the Downs at Gumber Corner, where the Stane Street crosses them, to see without the aid of any instrument, that the straight line from Chichester to Leith Hill, both of which are conspicuous from this point, passes far to the westward of one's position."

One can also see from the same spot, and without the aid of any instrument more complicated than a stick or umbrella stuck in the ground, that the line of the Stane Street, which is here absolutely intact and most conspicuous, does not point to Pulborough Bridge at all, but well to the left of it, about half way between the northern end of the bridge and the church on the top of the hill to the north of it.  Nor does it require an expert in topography to do so, the fact stares you in the face.

On page 69 :

" From the East gate of Chichester to Pulborough Bridge one direct alignment has been struck, the accuracy of which is the more remarkable from the fact that it crosses a range of hills between the two points, so that each end of this first limb is hidden from the other."

There is nothing remarkable about the accuracy of such an alignment, even if it did point at Pulborough Bridge, because, although each end of it is hidden from the other, both ends can be seen from the summit of the Downs near Gumber Corner where the Stane Street crosses them.

A magnificent view is obtained from this spot.  In a north-easterly direction Pulborough and Pulborough

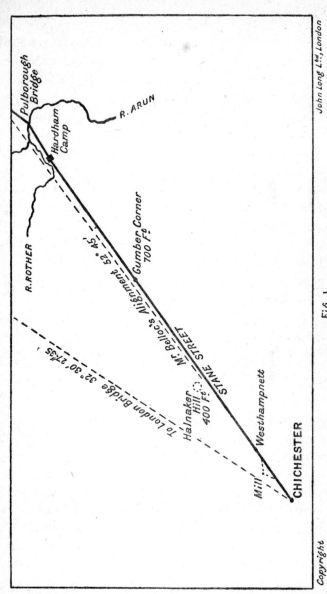

Fig. 1.

John Long Ltd., London

Pulborough Bridge

R. ARUN

Hardham Camp

R. ROTHER

Gumber Corner
700 Ft.

Mr Belloc's Alignment 52° 45′

STANE STREET

To London Bridge 32° 30′ 27″35

Halnaker Hill
400 Ft.

Westhampnett

Mill

CHICHESTER

Bridge are in plain view, with miles of country stretching away over the Weald to the distant sky lines of Leith Hill and Brockham Warren. In the opposite direction the sea plane of Chichester lies at one's feet, and the alignment carries the eye through Appledram, down the fairway of Chichester channel, past West Itchenor, and away to the Isle of Wight which is plainly visible on a clear day, so plainly in fact, that it is quite possible that the alignment in that direction may have been taken on to some conspicuous point on that sky-line. The summit of St. Catherine's Hill is almost exactly on that alignment; and although the spire of Chichester Cathedral is conspicuous from Gumber Corner, it was not there when the Stane Street was planned, and the East Gate could not be identified without the erection of a considerable mark. Again on page 242 Mr. Belloc says:

"The use of that common sense, without which history cannot be written, should be sufficient to convince anyone that Pulborough Bridge, as we now have it, corresponds exactly with the Roman crossing of the river, for coincidence could never account for the exact termination at this point of an alignment over 14 miles in length."

This is a typical example of the way in which Mr. Belloc mixes up fact with fiction. That the Roman road crossed the river at Pulborough Bridge I am not prepared to deny, but the proof of this must rest upon evidence other than coincidence, because the "alignment of over 14 miles in length" does not terminate at this point, or pass through it at all, but some 130 yards north-west of it. Anyone who takes the trouble to visit the spot can see this for himself at a glance; or it can easily be detected on a map of no larger scale than the 1-inch; or it can be proved mathematically. The curious thing is that Mr. Belloc apparently aims at, and even takes some pride in, extreme accuracy; because he constantly uses the words "exact," "exactly," or "precisely," but in connection with figures which are not even approximate.

So far I have dealt only with the alleged direction in which this alignment is supposed to point, namely the southern end of Pulborough Bridge. Even this approximate direction is quite sufficient for the identification of the road, and on this particular section of it the exact bearing of the alignment does not materially affect the theory of construction of the road as a whole, which is the final objective of this investigation. But since Mr. Belloc has assigned an angular value to this alignment, it may be well to inquire into this also.

On page 213 he says:

"The Stane Street starts, then, from what was the Roman and mediæval East Gate of Chichester; it sets out at an angle of $37\frac{1}{4}°$ N. or E. and pursues that direction . . . to the Summit of the Downs at Gumber Corner . . . it is an alignment drawn *exactly* towards the crossing of the Arun at Pulborough Bridge, and the reason which led the Roman engineers to lay down this alignment —was—the fact that it combined the easiest crossing of the Downs with a single passage over the water, avoiding the double passage that would have been necessary if the line had been deflected *by even a degree* to the north, for that would have involved the crossing of the Rother as well as the Arun."

It will be observed that a deflection to the north of even a degree would carry the road into serious trouble. Mr. Belloc's bearing is $37\frac{1}{4}°$ N. of E. equals 52° 45'. The mean bearing of the true alignment (i.e. to Gumber Corner and Hardham Camp) is 53° 54' 15".6, and to Pulborough Bridge 54° 4' 23".73, a deflection to the north of a little over 1° as compared with the true alignment and $1\frac{1}{4}°$ as compared with that on Pulborough Bridge.

On page 93 :

"A little further to the west and both the Arun and the Rother would have had to be crossed where their streams are numerous and meet in very difficult and wet ground."

Unfortunately this is the very ground over which Mr. Belloc's alignment of 52° 45' would pass (*see* Diagram Fig. 1, page 25) ; it is marked on the map "liable to floods." Such an alignment would not touch the Stane Street at all ; it would pass nearly quarter of a mile to the north-west of Hardham Camp and nearly 3 furlongs from Pulborough Bridge. The same paragraph continues :

"We must conclude that the line thus struck is the very best its engineers could have chosen."

No doubt the true alignment, 53° 48' 40"·54 is the very best, equally without doubt Mr. Belloc's alignment 52° 45' is the very worst, and affords some justification for his statement on page 144 that :

"Theories upon the line of the Roman roads are plotted out with an amazing assurance."

Before leaving this first alignment, and although strictly speaking outside the scope of my investigations, I must revert for a moment to the first of the two divergences of the modern road from the line of the Stane Street, referred to on page 13. This divergence is the "elbow" at Westhampnett Mill, of which Mr. Belloc says on page 177 :

"The cause of this I have found it impossible to discover, but its shape suggests encroachment."

There appears, however, to be a fairly obvious reason, or at least an obvious reason presents itself, though whether it is the true one or not, it is impossible to say.

The reason is this : Some 300 yards off the line of the Stane Street, and close to the " elbow " formed by the divergence in question is Westhampnett Mill, driven by water power from the Lavant River which runs close by. Milling being a dusty and thirsty occupation, and the waggoners or others who took their grist to or from the mill being thirsty people, the " Swan Inn " was established close to the Mill and exactly on this " elbow." The inference seems obvious —the track of the wagons, or of thirsty wayfarers going to or from the Mill or the " Swan," gradually developed into a made road ; the portion of the Stane Street, about half a mile long, between the points of divergence, gradually fell out of use, and the road via the " elbow " became the modern highway. (Fig. I, page 25.)

# II

# From the Southern End of Pulborough Bridge to the Shoulder of Leith Hill

THE second great limb is from Pulborough Bridge to the shoulder of Leith Hill, and I will describe this in Mr. Belloc's own words:

Page 58:

"The second limb from Pulborough Bridge to Leith Hill bends round towards the original line and runs but 22° 30′ east of the meridian. It is 17½ miles in length."

Page 69:

"From Pulborough Bridge, again, to a point on the shoulder of Leith Hill, a second alignment has been struck, one slight divergence in which will be discussed later."

I propose to reverse Mr. Belloc's procedure and to take this slight divergence first.

Page 97:

"This point of flexion occurs at the Southern End of a building called Todhurst Farm. It is *exactly* 3¾ miles from the Southern End of Pulborough Bridge, and these 3¾ miles may be regarded as a very short separate limb uniting the first long one which ends at Pulborough, with the second long one which ends at Leith Hill. The angle between this short " junction " and the main line, which runs absolutely straight from Todhurst Farm to the shoulder of Leith Hill, is one of seven degrees, the main line being directed 22° 30′ East of North and the short 3¾ miles from Pulborough Bridge to Todhurst Farm 29° 30′ East of North."

This short alignment from Pulborough Bridge to
Todhurst Farm is the only one of Mr. Belloc's alignments that points where he says it does ; it points,
it is true, to Todhurst Farm, but both the bearing
and the distance are incorrectly stated ; the mean
bearing is 32° 55′ 44″, not 29° 30′, and the distance is
2¾ miles, not 3¾ miles.

Page 245 :

" The Stane Street pursues this direction of 59°· North of East
for a distance of *exactly* 3¾ miles, reckoning from the South end of
the Bridge.  Its absolute straight line has been marred by *the
necessity of crossing the railway.*"

Here it will be noticed that the bearing is now said
to be 31° instead of 29° 30′ as stated above, and the
word " exactly " is applied to the distance containing
an error of 36 per cent.  What is meant by its absolute
straight line being " marred by the necessity of crossing
the railway " is something of a mystery, since the
writer is supposed to be referring to the Stane Street
or its alignment.  The former was probably built
some 1,500 years before railways were invented, and
the latter, being an imaginary line, would not be
affected in any case.  Presumably, therefore, this
refers to the modern road, but even that must have
been in existence long before railways ; and in any
case for the first mile or more from Pulborough Bridge
the modern road winds considerably and does not
begin to be straight till it reaches Puttock's Farm, half
a mile beyond the railway crossing.

With reference to this short secondary alignment
Mr. Belloc says on page 244 :

" It is remarkable that this alignment is taken, with a back
sight, towards the end of the bridge.  In other words the Roman
engineers did not plot out the Chichester to Pulborough section
and then plot out another section from the top of Pulborough Hill,

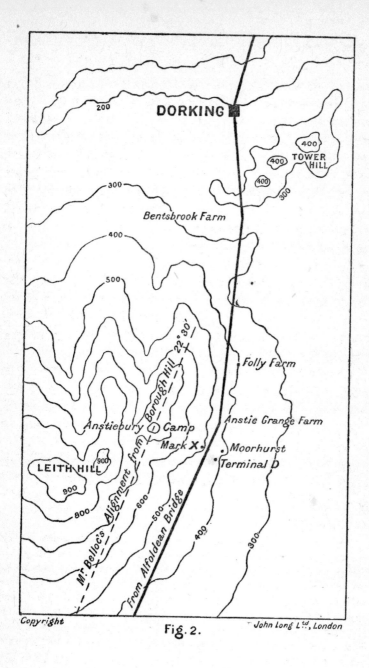

Fig. 2.

John Long L$^{td}$, London

but schemed for two straight lines that should have one definite point where they crossed, to wit, the southern end of the bridge."

Here, again, there appears to be nothing remarkable in this somewhat involved scheme. So far as I can understand it, it is merely a roundabout way of saying that the secondary alignment began where the first left off, that is supposing the first alignment to have been taken, as Mr. Belloc says, onto the southern end of Pulborough Bridge. But the first alignment is not on Pulborough Bridge, therefore the scheme of intersection at its southern end is based upon a fallacy as regards the alignments.

Returning now to the main alignment of the second limb, Mr. Belloc's bearing for this is 22° 30′ but the exact bearing is 24° 35′ 41″·22, an error of a little over two degrees. It will be noticed that Mr. Belloc's errors of alignment or bearings are by no means constant, so that whatever may have been his method of computation it must be a very defective one. An alignment of 22° 30′ would not touch the road at all, but go right away to the left, and, as in the case of the first limb, would lead over the very ground to be avoided ; in this case the steep summit of Anstiebury Camp at a height of 800 feet (*see* Diagram Fig. 2, page 33). The spot from which this alignment starts is described as follows.

Page 97 :

" Not quite a mile on the way north from Pulborough Bridge there will be noticed upon the right beyond the railway, a rather sharp eminence, which, though it does not form a summit of its group (and is only upon the side of the general slope upwards towards that summit at Redfold), is so placed as to afford a good view of Leith Hill, and to be seen clearly from Leith Hill against the sky. This point is just behind the farm-house known as New Place, and the eminence in question is known locally as Borough Hill. It was towards this point that the alignment from Leith Hill

was taken, and from this point towards Leith Hill that that alignment ran.".

The foregoing description is perfectly correct, and
I have quoted it at length because it is highly probable,
as I hope to show later on, that it was from there or
thereabouts that the great alignment from Pulborough
started.   But I shall also offer reasonable presumptive
evidence that this alignment was not taken onto Mr.
Belloc's mark X or terminal D. on the shoulder of
Leith Hill, but over the summit of Brockham Warren
(see folding map) straight to the southern end of Old
London Bridge.

Continuing on page 98 Mr. Belloc says :

" The precise point upon the shoulder of Leith Hill which was
chosen for the terminus of the second limb, was that spot upon
the eastern slope of Leith Hill which is just high enough to show
clearly above the rolling land of the Weald and yet just low enough
to come below the steep part of the slopes.   The Weald rises in
great billows up towards the county boundary, and a mark set
much below the 400 foot contour might be invisible, and would
always be doubtfully observable from the lower and distant part
of the district."

I do not think for a moment that this was the spot
selected by the Roman engineers, because, apart from
the fact that it is some 150 yards off the line of the
road, such experts as they were would hardly choose
a spot so low and of such doubtful visibility, when
the clearly defined sky-line of Brockham Warren was
right in front of them some 5 miles further on.   I
have already drawn attention to Mr. Belloc's propen-
sity for failing to discriminate between the road and
its alignment.

On page 101 he says :

" From the point close to Moorhurst, where the northern terminus
of the second limb was established, if you look forward in the direc-

tion of that limb and imagine the Stane Street continuing its old direction unchanged, you will discover that direction to point right at the steepest and highest part of the Box Hill Group. It makes for the precipitous slope of Brockham Warren, and for the very highest summit of those heights."

The most obvious place for setting up a mark for the alignment could hardly have been better described. Mr. Belloc's terminal point near Moorhurst is thus described on page 100 :

" A house called Moorhurst stands just above the four hundred foot contour on this eastern slope of Leith Hill and at the point just below where the slope begins to grow steep ; about 350 yards up from this farm, northward by a little *west*, and in a field which lies immediately south of a wood called Ryefield Copse, was set up the mark which formed a terminus, a northern terminus for the second limb coming from Borough Hill, near Pulborough, a southern terminus for the third short limb, which was plotted so as to take Dorking Gap."

This point is here emphatically described as that where the two limbs or alignments met. It is again described on page 259 :

" On a former page of this book (pages 97 to 100) I spoke of the point north and a little *east* of the house called Moorhouse which formed the terminal point where the alignment coming northwards from Borough Hill near Pulborough and the next alignment coming southwards from Dorking Gap met. But this point must be described in more detail than I then gave to it."

The description so far is that, on page 100 it is about 350 yards northward by a little *west*, and on page 259 northward and a little *east* from Moorhurst. As a matter of fact, it is neither the one nor the other, but about 350 yards *west* by a little *north* from Moorhurst (*see* Fig 2, page 33). Mr. Belloc then proceeds to describe in more detail this spot where the two alignments met. But in the course of this description,

and in the accompanying map on page 263, these
alignments are shown as meeting at Anstie Grange
Farm over quarter of a mile north-east of the previous
meeting point called X. Also in another map (Fig. 10,
page 103) these same two alignments are shown as
meeting at a point marked

"D = terminal point on Leith Hill,"

which is certainly not the meeting point X previously
described in such detail. It might possibly be Anstie
Grange Farm, but it is not marked as such, and there
is no mention of any terminal mark having been
erected there. But wherever the actual marks may
have been placed to or from which the alignments
were taken, there is one spot and one spot only which
satisfies the condition of being a "northern terminus
for the second limb" and at the same time "a southern
terminus for the third limb," viz., Anstie Grange
Farm where the two alignments meet, and with which
all other alignment marks of the two limbs concerned
must also have been in alignment. But Mr. Belloc's
mark X on the shoulder of Leith Hill is some 150
yards off the second alignment and 300 yards off the
third, and eventually it transpires that it is not the
terminal mark at all, although so minutely described
as such, but what he calls a "conjectural look-out
point" from which the placing of other "subsidiary"
marks is supposed to have been directed. I think we
are justified in assuming that this was not the method
adopted by the Roman engineers. Having considered
the three different directions that Mr. Belloc assigns
to this alignment,—first, along his bearing of 22° 30′
which takes it through Anstiebury Camp ; second,
onto the mark X or terminal D on Leith Hill ; and
finally onto Anstie Grange Farm ; and taking the

latter as that which is intended, I will now consider the claims of this alignment to acceptance.

On page 85 Mr. Belloc says :

"We may be certain that the crossing of the upper Arun at Alfoldean Bridge is due to the Roman engineers alone, for it comes right upon the exact line which aims from Pulborough Hill to the shoulder of Leith Hill."

From what has already been seen of Mr. Belloc's topographical work it will have been realised that wherever the word " exact " is used there is generally ground for suspicion, and in this case our suspicions are well founded.

What appears to have happened is this : It will be remembered that Mr. Belloc's short limb of $2\frac{3}{4}$ miles from Pulborough Bridge ends at Todhurst Farm, where a well-marked bend in the road occurs. The road continues on through Billingshurst, where another slight bend occurs—and from there the road is almost dead straight right away to Anstie Grange Farm. There is a very slight bend at Alfoldean Bridge which for the present may be ignored. But Mr. Belloc seems to have jumped to the conclusion that the road began to be straight at Todhurst Farm, and has taken his alignment accordingly from Borough Hill through that point to Anstie Grange Farm. The result is that the road immediately leaves his alignment at Todhurst Farm, and bears away to the right to Billingshurst, which is 200 yards off his alignment. From here the road and the alignment converge, meeting, theoretically at Anstie Grange Farm, but owing to slight divergence of the road, they meet, as a matter of fact, about half a mile short of that terminus. Alfoldean Bridge is about 150 yards off the alignment, which tends to show, not that the crossing here was not due to the Roman engineers alone, but that Mr. Belloc's alignment is not the right one. I am giving Mr. Belloc the benefit of supposing that his alignment was taken onto Anstie Grange Farm (or a mark in alignment with it). Had it been taken onto his mark on Leith Hill or along his bearing 22° 30′ it would never have touched the road again, and would have passed some 300 to 500 yards to the west of Alfoldean Bridge.

It appears to have been a fixed principle in the construction of these Roman roads to adhere so far as possible to a straight alignment, and, where a divergence became necessary, to return to the alignment at the earliest opportunity. Now if Mr. Belloc's alignment had been the correct one, there is no natural obstacle or difficulty of any sort which would have prevented the road from following it, or which, if a divergence through Billingshurst had been decided on, would have prevented it from rejoining the alignment. But the road does not do so ; it keeps straight on to Anstie Grange Farm.

There is yet another reason, perhaps the best of all.

In speaking of the alignment from Borough Hill to Leith Hill produced over Brockham Warren, Mr. Belloc says on page 101 :

"If you take a direct line from the same point (Leith Hill) to London Bridge it differs by less than one degree from a continuation of the second limb, and the same precipitous slope is met with.

In a footnote he adds :

"On which account one might maintain that the whole system from Pulborough Bridge to London Bridge was ultimately based on one great alignment. I doubt it. The coincidence is not absolute."

It does not seem to have occurred to Mr. Belloc that the reason why the coincidence is not absolute is that his own alignment is wrong. Had he been aware of the fact that an alignment from Borough Hill near Pulborough to the southern end of Old London Bridge passes exactly through Alfoldean Bridge and the site of the Camp there (*see* folding map) he might perhaps have reconsidered his opinion, and given the Roman engineers credit for a beautifully co-ordinated scheme.

# III

# From the Shoulder of Leith Hill to Juniper Hill

THE third limb is that which negotiates Dorking Gap; from Leith Hill, or rather from Anstie Grange Farm, to Juniper Hill, and passes through the crossing of the river Mole at Burford Bridge.

The idea here occurs to me that the selection by the Roman engineers of Burford Bridge for the crossing of the Mole may possibly have been influenced by the facility afforded to their young officers for taking their girls out to lunch at the popular hotel there, but Mr. Belloc's " exact " measurements have failed to produce any confirmation of what, I fear, must be regarded as mere conjecture.

But to continue—on page 60 Mr. Belloc says:

" The third limb from Leith Hill to the crossing of Juniper Hill is a short one of 6¾ miles, designed to negotiate Dorking Gap, and to avoid the steep edge of Box Hill."

And in a footnote he adds:

" If we count from one " sighting point " to another, the end of this third limb is a point on Juniper Hill, making the limb one mile and more longer."

What is meant by this I cannot understand. No matter where we count *from*, the end of this third limb is the point C on Juniper Hill already described, and marked on his map (Fig. 10, page 103). It is, of course, quite optional to start measuring where you please, but so far as the length of this limb is concerned it can have only one starting point, viz. : where the last limb terminated at Anstie Grange Farm, and only one finishing point, viz., point C. Moreover, on page 102 he says :

" They fixed their new terminal at the point C, in what is now Juniper Wood. It stood five miles and six furlongs from their existing terminal D, upon the shoulder of Leith Hill."

But we have just been told that the length of this limb is $6\frac{3}{4}$ miles, and " one mile or more longer " if we measure to a point one mile or more further off, but since we are given no clue to any " sighting point " other than point C, I must confess my inability to follow the writer's meaning. The alignment continued to $7\frac{3}{4}$ or even $6\frac{3}{4}$ miles from terminal D, would carry us far beyond the limits of the third limb, and right away from the fourth to the low ground East of Leatherhead which would be invisible from terminal D.

Again we are told on page 260 :

" The straight line of the southern alignment from Pulborough and Alfoldean northward, and so through Ockley, strikes exactly the gate between Anstie Grange Farm and its barn, and from precisely the same spot the next, or northern limb, that negotiates Dorking Gap, takes its rise." [1]

I have already remarked that what is called terminal D might possibly be Anstie Grange Farm, although it is not marked so on the map (Fig. 10, page 103) and from the above it would appear to be so. But the distance from Anstie Grange Farm to point C on Juniper Hill is barely $5\frac{1}{2}$ miles, so now it appears that

[1] It has already been pointed out that Mr. Belloc's alignment does not pass through either Alfoldean or Ockley.

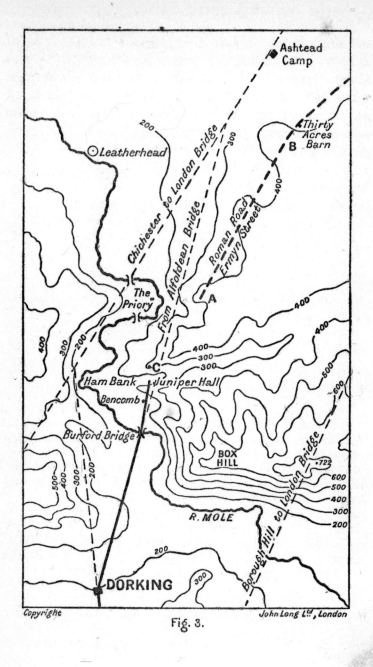

Fig. 3.

John Long Ltᵈ, London

terminal D is not Anstie Grange Farm after all, but quarter of a mile south of it. So that we have been given three different points of intersection for the same two alignments; exclusive of Anstiebury Camp on the alignment 22° 30′. First, the mark X on the shoulder of Leith Hill; second, terminal D, and finally Anstie Grange Farm, where in fact they do meet. The distance from mark X is 5 miles and 6 furlongs, but where the 6¾ miles, or that "one mile or more longer," come in, I am quite unable to discover. I think the 6¾ must be meant for 5¾ which is the same thing as 5 miles and 6 furlongs, the distance being measured from point X or terminal D, instead of Anstie Grange Farm. But although Anstie Grange Farm is clearly the point of intersection of the two alignments there is no mention of any mark having been set up there, in fact, this is expressly denied, which confirms the conclusion that this is not the position of terminal D. The quotation on page 60 continues:

"From this it might be imagined that the high scaffolding and pole, or whatever other mark was used for drawing the alignments from distant point to distant point, was set up by the Roman engineers precisely at this spot (Anstie Grange Farm). But it is not likely that this was the case. Anyone visiting the locality will see why. All this shoulder of Leith Hill is a difficult one to turn. It presents no one conspicuous point from which a commanding observation could be taken north and south—at least not one point upon the fairly flat shelf below the last steep rise to the summit. This shelf is undulating, and any mark set up on one of its hollows would be hidden from the north and the south unless it were very high indeed. On the other hand, a mark set well up on the hill (as for instance, on the 800-foot summit, which is included in Anstiebury Camp itself) would have led the road far too high up the steep hill-side and condemned travel to a useless and even dangerous labour. What would seem to have been done is this: just where the steep part of the hill begins, there is an open field lying immediately under the wood called

Ryefield Copse. Thence a moderate scaffolding commands a view to the north and to the south. From this point of vantage [1] which is well above the 500-foot contour, the engineers would seem to have directed the placing of somewhat lower marks, one to the north the other to the south—the one to the south commanding the view over the Weald, but hidden from Dorking Gap; the one to the north commanding the Dorking Gap but hidden from the Weald. The southern one was perhaps fixed upon the ridge immediately behind Bearehurst at a height of some 450 feet. The northern one may well have stood on the high ground rather more than half a mile to the north, which all but touches the 500 foot contour and exactly corresponds to the long spinney lying east of Folly Farm in South Holmwood."

These are the sort of difficulties that Mr. Belloc delights in raising for no apparent reason, other than that of displaying his undoubted facility in contour work by a hypothetical method of overcoming them. They might easily have been avoided by taking the alignment onto Brockham Warren, and I cannot think that this third limb was plotted by any such complicated and clumsy method as he suggests.

On page 100 he says :

" The third short limb which negotiates the Dorking Gap is the most tricky part of the road and the one that needs the closest examination if we are to understand how it was plotted out."

Here for the first time I find myself in agreement with Mr. Belloc, not because there need be any great difficulty in plotting the alignment, supposing his mark on Juniper Hill to have been its true objective, but because this is indeed the most tricky part of the road, and it is within the last mile of this short limb that the real crux of the problem arises, namely, to determine the actual course of the road from Burford Bridge onwards. If the " closest examination " is

[1] This is the point previously described with such insistence as the terminus and point of junction of the second and third limbs.

given to it, there will be found at least reasonable probability for the conjecture that, after crossing the Mole at Burford Bridge, or possibly even before, the Stane Street did not follow the course which he assigns to it, and that the straight 2 miles of road which commences at point A on Mickleham Downs, as described on a previous page, was not part of the Stane Street at all. But the alternatives involved in this conjecture will be fully discussed when we come to consider the true alignments. At present we are considering Mr. Belloc's.

The road through Dorking Gap must of necessity have been somewhat winding ; it is only 5½ miles in length, and is merely a connecting link between the section of the road coming northward from Pulborough and that coming southward from London, so that there does not seem to be much necessity for a single hard and fast alignment. It is more than probable that the site of the camp at Dorking was decided upon in the course of the preliminary survey which must have preceded the planning of the road, and a mark erected there, so that all the Roman engineers had to do was to make for this mark, a bare 3 miles away, surely not a very difficult problem.

In considering the difficulties that the Roman engineers had to contend with, it must be remembered that they were experts at this particular kind of work, and that they probably had a Corps of Surveyors and Signallers highly trained in the running of these long alignments. It may be taken as certain that they had no telescopic sights, but, on the other hand, it is not unlikely that the atmosphere at that period may have been much clearer than it is now. (The recent coal strike was a revelation in the matter of visibility.) Also it is more than likely that the range of human vision, especially that of the native barbarians whose services were possibly requisitioned for the purpose, may have been vastly superior to that of the present day, and of course, only men with exceptionally good eyesight would have been employed. I have, myself, known men, especially among the North-Sea fishermen, many of whom go as yacht hands in the summer-time, who could pick up a mark, such as a buoy, at sea, just as well or even better with the naked eye than I could do with a powerful field-glass. It seems reasonable, therefore, to conclude that, under the conditions prevailing some 1,500 years ago, and over the distances in question, the absence of telescopic sights was not such a serious disadvantage as might be supposed, and that these long sights from summit to summit did not present any very serious difficulty. Also in the matter of instruments, a fairly long sight vane having a fine slit at one end and a horse-hair or fine thread at the other, and mounted on a graduated circle of fairly large diameter, would have been an instrument quite within the capacity of the Roman engineers to make, and would, I think, have provided a fairly efficient substitute for the modern theodolite. Even so simple a device as a plumb line suspended from an arm of some sort and viewed through a fine slit, or small hole, at a few yards distance, is one with which very accurate alignments can be ranged. Nor is it, I think, too much to suppose that they may have had some kind of reflecting instrument in the nature of the heliograph, by which the rays of the sun could be projected over long distances, and received at the other end.[1]

---

[1] I am indebted to Major-General Sir George Barker, K.C.B., for the information that the Romans had a trained body of Surveyors called GROMATICI, who used an instrument resembling the theodolite called the DIOPTRA, which was improved under Trajan.

But reverting for a moment to the previous quotation which describes the position of the " secondary " mark for negotiating Dorking Gap, which, he says :

" All but touches the five hundred foot contour and *exactly* corresponds to the long spinney lying *east* of Folly Farm."

If the reader cares to look at the map (Fig 2, page 33) he will find that Folly Farm is exactly on the 400-foot contour, and that the ground slopes down from west to east, so that any point lying east of Folly Farm must be on a still lower level. Yet Mr. Belloc says that this point " all but touches the 500-foot contour." The fact, of course, is that the long spinney referred to lies *west* not *east* of Folly Farm. This is another of those careless mistakes which are of such frequent occurrence throughout the book.

The bearing assigned to this alignment is 7° 30′ instead of 6° 34′ the error being just under one degree, but in the opposite direction this time, i.e. the angle is too large instead of too small, and the alignment would pass to the right of Burford Bridge instead of through it. This concludes the third alignment.

## IV

# From Juniper Hill to the Southern End of Old London Bridge

WE now enter upon the fourth and last Act of this " Comedy of Errors " in which, as in good comedy it should, the fun reaches its climax.

It will be remembered that in speaking of the second alignment produced, Mr. Belloc said :

" It makes for the precipitous slope of Brockham Warren, and for the very highest summit of those heights. It was the business of the Roman engineers, of course, to avoid such a difficulty as that, and to turn it."

Page 102 :

" What they did therefore was to look for a conspicuous point, not too high, upon the shoulder of the Box Hill group, and this they discovered a little above the 300-foot contour upon the slope of the promontory marked AB upon the accompanying sketch. (this has nothing to do with the " point A ") And they fixed their new terminal at the point C, in what is now Juniper Wood."

Page 102 :

" To that point C was their alignment of the third limb drawn, and from it, as we shall see later, the alignment of the fourth limb was taken, which led that fourth limb from C to London Bridge."

Hitherto the exact position of point C has not been investigated, because, for the purpose of the third short limb through Dorking Gap, this was of no great importance, since the alignment was assumed to be through two known points, Anstie Grange Farm and Burford Bridge. But as a starting point for the fourth alignment, we must fix its position as exactly as possible. For this purpose Mr. Belloc's three different terminals and incorrect bearing and distances are absolutely useless, but fortunately the conformation of the ground comes to our assistance.

We are told that point C is just above the 300-foot contour. Now the spur of Juniper Hill over which the alignment takes us, is only just above that same contour (Fig. 3, page 43); in fact the distance from the 300-foot level on the upward grade to the corresponding level on the downward grade, after crossing the ridge, is little over 100 yards, so that point C must lie somewhere within that 100 yards, and if we take the very crest of the ridge, the most obvious position, we have point C located within a yard or two.

Page 106 :

" The Stane Street and its theoretical alignment from the terminus in Juniper Hill Wood onto London Bridge, do not coincide until we reach an unmistakable point A just above the 400-foot contour and exactly 500 yards south-east of Cherkeley Court. There the winding way suddenly becomes dead straight for two full miles, and *exactly coincides* with the alignment in question."

Here we have our old friend " exactly " again, with the result that might be expected. The point A is unmistakable enough, and there is no difficulty in determining the Azimuth of the straight 2 miles which we will call A–B (Fig. 3, page 43). But the coincidence of A–B with " its theoretical alignment " onto London Bridge " is as theoretical as the alignment itself. The point A is not on the alignment from C to London Bridge, or from C to Merton Abbey, nor does A–B

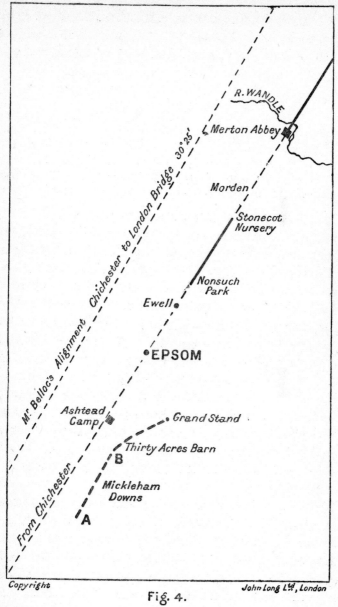

Fig. 4.

John Long Lᵗᵈ, London

take a line of its own to London Bridge. It does not point to London Bridge at all, but approximately to Merton Abbey, and 5 furlongs west of London Bridge (Fig. 4, page 51).

On page 60 :

" . . . the fourth limb . . . begins to be straight from a point in Mickleham Downs, it is aligned backwards towards Juniper Hill, and points straight to London Bridge ; it is driven at an angle under 28° 15' east of the meridian, and therefore converges with the ideal straight line from Chichester to London (which it meets at the foot of the Bridge) on a very fine angle."

The only part of this statement that is true is that the road begins to be straight at a point on Mickleham Downs and converges with the line from Chichester to London on a fine angle. The alignment of A–B backwards cuts the third alignment at a point nearly 3 furlongs south of point C, just east of the house called Bencomb (Fig. 3, page 43). The angle at which it is driven is not under 28° 15' but just over 29° and it is supposed to be pointing at London Bridge, the true bearing of which is 30° 37' 4". It converges with the ideal straight line from Chichester to London on a fine angle, but not so fine by some two degrees as Mr. Belloc's figures represent, and finally it meets this ideal straight line, not at the foot of London Bridge, but near Merton Abbey, about 8 miles from London Bridge.

Mr. Belloc insists with somewhat wearisome reiteration upon the exactitude of his alignments, and, at the risk of boring the reader, I must give a few more quotations, since these serve to emphasise the " amazing assurance " (to quote his own words) with which he jumps to conclusions, without taking the trouble to verify them, and gives bearings and distances as " exact " when they are not even approximate.

Page 70 :

" The Stane Street, as I shall hope to show later, is aligned upon a fourth great limb, absolutely straight, which reaches its northern terminus at London Bridge."

Page 112 :

" The last and much most weighty argument is the fact that for the first two miles and more from the terminus, the direct alignment points, not approximately towards, but *right at*, London Bridge ; and this can no more be a coincidence than can the direct pointing of the alignment over the South Downs towards Pulborough Bridge. This seems to me an argument so clearly convincing that it hardly needs support."

So it might be convincing if it were true, but unfortunately it isn't ; neither of these alignments points where Mr. Belloc says it does. The first does not point at Pulborough Bridge but at Hardham Camp, the terminus of the first day's march out of Chichester ; and the second points a little south of Merton Abbey, the probable terminus of the first day's march out of London.

Page 133–4 :

" . . . Supposing the road followed its normal straight line to London Bridge, the straight line along which it points where it was last visible . . . we may, following that road, make certain conjectures as to the site of the fourth station upon the analogy of the other three . . . and this takes us . . . to the crossing of the river Wandle in the neighbourhood of what was, for centuries, Merton Abbey."

Page 139 :

" Conjecture, then, points to the crossing of the Wandle by Merton Abbey as the site of the fourth and last Mansio upon the line between Chichester and London."

So that, after all that has been said about the absolute exactitude with which it points at London Bridge, it would now appear that Mr. Belloc knows perfectly well that it points towards Merton Abbey. Yet only a few pages further on (151) he says:

"The alignment from the corner of Juniper Hill across the Wandle points as absolutely at the southern end of Old London Bridge as any measurements will allow."

According to that, the crossing of the Wandle must be on the alignment from Juniper Hill to London Bridge, but, as a matter of fact, it isn't. It is on the direct alignment from Chichester to London Bridge. (Fig 4, page 51). In fact, on page 281 he says:

"The strict alignment taken from Epsom Downs to Old London Bridge carries us over the Wandle precisely at Merton."

That Mr. Belloc should have failed to discover that Merton is over quarter of a mile west of the alignment on London Bridge, or that an alignment on Merton Abbey passes 5 furlongs west of London Bridge, does not say much for the accuracy of the measurement, or the competence of the measurer. It reminds me of a small boy at school who swore he had run the 100 yards in 10 seconds. When questioned as to the timing of this wonderful performance, he said he had timed himself by the great college clock. I have forgotten the name of the boy, but any old Fettesian of the middle 'seventies who chances to read this book may possibly recall the incident, of which I have a clear recollection.

But to resume—on page 269 Mr. Belloc says:

"Luckily, however, that part of the road which can be certainly established has been preserved in a situation where *an exact alignment pointing to London Bridge can be proved*, and this, with a number of other circumstances to which I shall refer the problem, gives us the ground we have for believing the road to have *crossed the Wandle at Merton*."

Here, as in the case of the Chichester–Pulborough

alignment, it is not disputed that the road crossed the Wandle at Merton. What is disputed, and what Mr. Belloc makes no attempt to prove, for the very sufficient reason that it isn't true, is that the alignment from Juniper Hill to Merton Abbey and the direction of the road A–B points at London Bridge.

That A–B does not point anywhere near London Bridge may be demonstrated as follows. The Geographical Co-ordinates (Appendix C) are :—

|  | Latitude | Longitude |
|---|---|---|
|  | ° ′ ″ | ° ′ ″ |
| London Bridge . . . | 51 30 22·2 | 0 05 08·65 |
| Point A . . . . . | 51 16 22·1 | 0 18 26·60 |
| Difference . . . | 14′ 0″·1 =840″·1 | 13′ 17″·95 =797″·95 |
| Point B . . . . . | 51 17 43·1 | 0 17 15 |
| Point A . . . . . | 51 16 22·1 | 0 18 26·6 |
| Difference . . . | 1′ 21″·0 =81″ | 1′ 11″·6 =71″·6 |

The proportion of Longitude to Latitude on the alignment A–B is therefore $\frac{71\cdot6}{81}$.

If now we produce A–B to a point $x$ at the Latitude of London Bridge the difference of Longitude of $x$ from point A will be

$$\frac{840\cdot1 \times 71\cdot6}{81} = 742″\cdot61.$$

But the difference of Longitude from point A to London Bridge is

$$797\cdot95$$
$$742\cdot61$$

Diff. Long. $x$ and London Bridge $\underline{55″\cdot34}$.

Therefore $x$ is 55″·34 west of London Bridge. The linear value of 1″ of Longitude at the Latitude of London Bridge is nearly 21·1 yards and 55·34 × 21·1 = 5 furlongs and 67 yards.

The above method is only approximate, but near enough for demonstration. The true distance is just under 5 furlongs, but even this can hardly be regarded as pointing " as absolutely at the southern end of Old London Bridge as any measurements will allow."

Summing up what we have been told about this fourth alignment—in the diagram on page 59 (Fig. 3) it is marked :

" fourth limb 26° 30′ E. of N.'

On page 60 it is given as :

" Under 28° 15′."

On page 274 it is called :

" Just under 29°."

And on page 284 :

" As nearly as possible 28° 54′ east of the meridian or 60° 6 North of East."

And finally in the map at the end of the book it is marked

" 3rd alignment "

and is actually drawn to London Bridge.

With regard to the length of this fourth limb, on page 285 it is stated to be :

" 33,050 yards—within a few yards more or less,"

or fifty yards over 18¾ miles. But in the footnote on page 52, in discussing the probability of the Stane Street having crossed the Thames at a ferry 300 yards east of London Bridge, Mr. Belloc says :

" The error requiring an alignment with the ferry to the east would be one of 300 yards. This error in a trajectory of 18½ miles is one in a hundred (3 in 309·76) "

that makes the distance 30,976 yards. But 18½ miles = 32,560 yards, and we have just been told that the distance is 33,050, so that we have three different distances assigned to this limb, viz., 30,976 yards ; 32,560 yards ; and 33,050 yards. We have also had four different bearings, and two different directions assigned to it, and it has been called the third as well as the fourth limb. Surely this must break all previous records for carelessness and inaccuracy. Continuing the footnote on page 52 regarding the error of one in a hundred in what he calls a " trajectory " of 18½ miles, Mr. Belloc says :

" That is a very marked divergence. It would mean in angular measurement over half a degree, an appreciable angle even without instruments or precision."

But in this same " trajectory " Mr. Belloc himself makes an error, not of one hundred yards or one in a hundred, but of 5 furlongs, or one in thirty, representing over one and a half degrees in angular measurement. And yet on page 283 he says :

" I have taken measurements *as accurate as were in my power*, and I think I can show that the degree of precision with which the alignment points at Old London Bridge is far greater than has been, or might be, imagined."

But all we are offered by way of proof is four different angles, three different distances, and two different directions.

On the same page he says :

" As no more than two miles (or a little less) of the original road remains visible, and that at the end of the alignment furthest from London Bridge, it might be doubted, at first sight, whether the coincidence upon which my alignment is based can be properly established."

It is only at first sight that the existence of such a coincidence can be entertained at all ; but the above remark, together with the previous one about the precision of the alignment being " greater than has been or might be imagined," is rather illuminating. Such remarks would never have been made by a competent topographer, because in computing the Azimuth and distance it makes not the slightest difference at which end of the alignment the straight 2 miles of road occur, and the plotting of the exact alignment is not a matter of imagination or guess-work, but of mathematical certainty. Two miles or less is amply sufficient for determining the alignment of a " trajectory " under 19 miles in length, nor is it at all necessary that the whole, or any part, of those 2 miles should be visible. If only a single stone at one end and a single stone at the other end can be identified as belonging to Stane Street, it is all that is required, and the Azimuth can be calculated to a fraction of a second, and the distance to a fraction of a foot.

Mr. Belloc says :

" An old road is not a mathematical line. It has breadth and its edges are sometimes broken."

That is so, but an alignment *is* a mathematical line, and one whose position cannot be varied to suit the exigencies of any particular hypothesis, as Mr. Belloc has done with several of his so-called align-ments. But the alignment in question would not be measured on the spot, but computed from the geo-graphical co-ordinates ascertained from the six-inch Ordnance Map, on the margins of which the Latitude and Longitude are marked to every 30″ of Latitude and 1′ of Longitude.

Some further light is thrown on Mr. Belloc's methods by the following—speaking of the length of the line A–B he says on page 284 :

" The line, which is absolutely unswerving, can be followed in the clearest fashion from summit to summit until one reaches the top of the hill above Thirty Acres Barn. The total distance from the one point to the other *I make* to be 3,484 yards, and the angle at which the perfectly direct line of these 3,484 yards is driven *I make* to be *as nearly as possible* 28 degrees 54 minutes east of the meridian."

The angle and the distance will both depend upon the exact position of the terminal points, and these Mr. Belloc determines for himself ; but having once done so, the computation of Azimuth and distance is one that admits of no ambiguity or variation. Incidentally I may mention that at a distance of 3,484 yards from point A, the road has ceased to be straight and has already begun to bend to the right, which brings Mr. Belloc's point B appreciably off the alignment of the road from A.

Mr. Belloc continues :

" Now what limit of error is one to allow in this measurement ? It is a matter, of course, for the judgment of anyone who chooses to visit this spot, and to notice how the line can be followed from summit to summit."

It is nothing of the sort ; it is not a matter of judgment at all, but of mathematical computation, and if it were a matter of judgment, it is one of which no one but a topographical surveyor would be a competent judge.

As to the limit of error to be allowed, there need be no error in the mathematical computation, but the accuracy of the result would depend on the accuracy with which the Latitude and Longitude of the terminal points can be plotted on the map, and on the accuracy of the map itself. We may accept the accuracy of the six-inch Ordnance Map as the utmost that is humanly possible, i.e. no detectable error is allowed; and any point can be plotted on it to within a 6-foot circle—the size of a small flower bed; and this may be regarded as the limit of error.

It might perhaps interest Mr. Belloc to know that, in the East Africa Protectorate Survey 1906 and 1911, the limit of error allowed in the Base Measurement was $\dfrac{1}{200,000}$ and the degree of accuracy obtained was $\dfrac{1}{304,300}$ using steel tapes, and with invar wires in catenary $\dfrac{1}{1,400,000}$ an accuracy I should imagine undreamt of in his philosophy.

(*Text Book of Topographical Surveying*, Colonel Close.)

Again regarding the total distance he says on page 285:

"The total distance, *I make* to be 33,050 yards within a very few yards more or less. Here *the uncertainty is of no vast importance to a hundred yards or so*, for the one three hundredth more or less in the length of so exceedingly prolonged a triangle (*sic*) is of no appreciable effect in the measurement of its angles. The distance is certainly over 33,000 yards and certainly under 33,100."

(The exact distance 33,015·766 yards.)

How an alignment comes to be a triangle I don't quite know, but the above is a most amazing statement from one professing a knowledge of topography. The use of such expressions as " I make to be as nearly as possible " with regard to an angle which is only expressed to the nearest minute of arc, and " I make to be—within a very few yards more or less " as applied to a distance, is wholly inadmissible in an investigation of this sort where exactitude is, as the lawyers would say, " of the essence of the contract."

Moreover, the " bearings " which Mr. Belloc " makes to be as nearly as possible," so and so, are not true Azimuths, and it is only from a true Azimuth that the course of a true alignment can be computed, and plotted on the map. I have already hazarded a guess as to how Mr. Belloc's " bearings " were arrived at. His distances do not seem to have been calculated at all, but measured on the map itself, by fitting the successive sheets together, or by adding together the measurements on separate sheets ; and the alignments have not been " plotted " mathematically but, apparently, drawn with a string on the sheets so fitted together or plotted on " Mercator " or " mean bearing " courses. Such methods, of course, are hopelessly inaccurate. In the first place, as already pointed out, a straight line or a " Mercator Course " on the map does not coincide by several hundred yards with a true alignment such as from Chichester to London. And further, apart from the fact that the sheets of the map are liable to considerable distortion under varying conditions of temperature, humidity, etc., and as a result of being handled—it is not humanly possible to fit a number of sheets together with such exactitude as to be a reliable basis of measurement, whether angular or linear.[1]

For the purpose of exact investigation measurements can only be relied upon within the limits of individual sheets, and such measurements must be made from the scale engraved upon the sheet itself, since the scale will conform to any expansion or contraction

[1] Such distortion occurs even on the Admiralty charts which are mounted on linen, and is sometimes a source of appreciable error.

that may occur. Moreover, an approximate computation, which would be much nearer than the results so obtained, can be made in a few minutes by those who know how to do it, and even the exact computation could be made in a fraction of the time it would take to fit the sheets together, and take, and add up, the measurements.

If Mr. Belloc's bearings and distances be co-ordinated as a " closed traverse," it will be found that even on his own figures there is a closing error of nearly a mile, while as compared with the correct figures, the closing error is over $2\frac{1}{4}$ miles.

The last thing to be criticised is the folding map at the end of the book, which is not a map at all but a pure fabrication, drawn to give effect to Mr. Belloc's inaccurate measurements, and hypothetical alignments. All the bearings are wrong, and all the distances of doubtful accuracy; consequently, all the positions marked on it are incorrectly placed, and the so-called " map " is merely diagrammatic, showing the relative positions, but these only approximately. If, for example, we assume the position of Chichester to be the starting point, London Bridge is about $2\frac{1}{4}$ miles out of its true position, and all the other points and alignments in proportion to their respective degrees of error. The last alignment from Juniper Hill, which is the fourth, is marked the third, and the alignment of the straight 2 miles of road A–B which points to Merton Abbey has been drawn to London Bridge. But in order to meet the requirement that the road crosses the Wandle at Merton Abbey, the position of the latter has been deliberately moved fully half a mile to the east of its true position (according to the scale of the map) so as to bring it onto the alignment from A to London Bridge.

Not only so, but the straight pieces of the Clapham Road and Kennington Road which are known to be on the alignment from Merton to London have been similarly moved, in fact, the whole 7 miles from Merton to London Bridge has been fabricated so as to conform to Mr. Belloc's fictitious alignment. Finally, by an appropriate coincidence, this so-called " map " is dated April 1st, 1912. Several of the sketch maps in the text have been constructed on similar principles, and, as a whole, the topographical work throughout the book is absolutely worthless for the purpose of exact investigation.

It is extremely to be regretted that a book so pleasantly written, of such undoubted interest, and archæological value, and involving such an immense amount of laborious research, should have been marred by such gross topographical blunders.

If I seem to have handled Mr. Belloc somewhat severely, it is, I think, no more than he deserves, in view of the fact that his book is supposed to rank as a standard work and textbook—that the exactitude of his measurements is insisted upon throughout—that the hypotheses of other writers are said to be put forward with " amazing assurance " ; and that he regards himself as a competent critic of the Ordnance Maps, and " the Cartography of Europe."

# THE TRUE ALIGNMENTS

IN considering the true alignments, we may now discard all these troublesome figures, since what we want to get at is, not the precise angular value assigned to this or that alignment, or the exact distance from one point to another, but the known points, or places on the map, through which these alignments pass, or from and to which they point ; remembering always that an " alignment " is an imaginary line, absolutely straight, and of indefinite length. It has no beginning or ending, being, in fact, the path of a ray of light, passing through two or more given points.

From the foregoing analysis of Mr. Belloc's alignments it will have been seen that he does not appear to have arrived at any definite conclusion, nor has he formulated any definite scheme as to the general principles on which the Stane Street was planned. But it may be taken as certain that such practical and methodical people as the Roman engineers would not carry out such a work by any such haphazard methods as those we have just been investigating. What Mr. Belloc appears to have done was to start off from Chichester along the known course of the road, groping his way as it were from point to point, and endeavouring, with the aid of the Ordnance maps, and his undoubted facility in contour work, to establish various terminal points at which marks

E

may possibly have been set up for the purpose of the alignments, and which, by dint of a good deal of " fudging," might be made to conform to his own preconceived ideas. But what we have to do, I think, is to try and put ourselves in the position of the Roman engineers before there was any road at all ; to consider the difficulties with which they were confronted, and to endeavour to reconstruct in our minds the principles by which they would be guided in carrying out their task, and their method of setting about it.

When we consider the network of roads with which the Romans covered the southern part of England, in conjunction with the advanced stage of their civilisation as indicated by their buildings, their literature, and their arts, we must, I think, concede that their engineers were capable of carrying out extensive surveys, and of constructing maps of a very fair degree of accuracy ; and that before the Stane Street was undertaken at all, the whole country between London and the sea must have been surveyed.

Their object then being to build a road from London to Chichester, the first and obvious thing to do would be to run an alignment from point to point. For this purpose they have the commanding heights of Leith Hill and the South Downs right on their track. Mr. Belloc dismisses, as not worth considering, the possibility of such an alignment having been plotted, and an alignment from London to Pulborough is similarly dismissed because it does not quite coincide with his own hypothetical alignment. But it seems to me inconceivable that the Roman engineers should have failed to take advantage of the heights of the Leith Hill and Box Hill groups, at approximately half way, from whose commanding summits the running of such alignments would have been child's play to such experts as they were. Without running an alignment from London to Chichester I do not see how they could decide whether the direct route (which they would follow so far as possible) were practicable or no. Well, let us, for the sake of argument, assume that this was done, and that the difficulties encountered, which have been sufficiently indicated on a previous page, were such as to suggest the advisability of looking for an alternative route.

It would not take them long to discover that the easiest passage of the South Downs was that ultimately adopted, via Gumber Corner.

Again, from Gumber Corner the shortest way would be a direct line to London Bridge, and this too would be plotted. But here again, the steep slopes of Leith Hill present a formidable objection to the more direct way. The grounds I have for supposing that a straight line from Gumber Corner to London was not only entertained, but actually plotted, are not purely hypothetical, but are based upon the following considerations.

An alignment from Gumber Corner to Old London Bridge passes right through the middle of Dorking and through the supposed site of the camp there, also through the N.W. corner of the churchyard, where the road has been identified, so that we have the following very remarkable coincidences of alignment.

An alignment from old London Bridge to the East Gate of Chichester passes through the bridge over the Wandle and the camp at Merton Abbey, the first day's march out of London. An alignment from London Bridge to the summit of the South Downs at Gumber Corner passes through the camp at Dorking, at the end of the second day's march. An alignment from London Bridge to Borough Hill near Pulborough passes through the camp at Alfoldean Bridge, at the end of the third day's march; and the alignment from the East Gate of Chichester to Borough Hill near Pulborough passes through Hardham Camp, at the end of the first day's march out of Chichester, or the fourth from London. So that in every case we find a " great alignment " passing through the middle of a Camp, and the three main alignments form what in topography is called a " closed traverse," i.e. a series of straight alignments which return to, or " close " upon their starting point. In this case the alignments being three in number form the triangle, London—Chichester—Pulborough—London (*see* folding map).

My other reason for thinking that an alignment from Gumber Corner to London was plotted out, is that, had the Roman engineers decided in the first instance on the Pulborough route, and to cross the Arun river at the bridge there, there seems no reason why they should not have taken their alignment onto the bridge as Mr. Belloc assumes they did. By doing so the road would have crossed the shoulder of Halnaker Hill and Gumber Corner at a slightly lower level, and I cannot believe that the Roman engineers would have gone out of their way to cross at a higher level than was absolutely necessary, without some very good reason.

Now the idea of a direct road from Gumber Corner to London supplies that reason, viz., that with London as their objective they would not diverge to the eastward further than they could help. But having abandoned the direct route and decided to go on via Pulborough, and having found a suitable site for their camp at Hardham exactly on the first alignment, they stuck to that alignment, and made a slight divergence from Hardham Camp to the crossing of the Arun.

Or possibly the site of the Camp may have been decided first in the course of the preliminary survey, and the alignment taken onto it in spite of the slight extra climb. But whichever way we take it, there is no getting away from the fact that the line of the Stane Street from Chichester to Gumber Corner points exactly at Hardham Camp and not at Pulborough Bridge.

Such then, is the perfectly symmetrical and co-ordinated scheme on which I believe the Stane Street to have been planned, viz., on a closed traverse comprising the three great alignments, London–Chichester–Pulborough–London, with perhaps an intermediate alignment from Gumber Corner to London Bridge passing through the camp at Dorking.

The first two of these great alignments exactly coincide with the first stages of the Stane Street from London and Chichester respectively, and of these little more need be said.

The third great alignment from Pulborough to London has of necessity been subject to some modification, owing to the divergence through Dorking Gap to avoid a crossing over Brockham Warren, but I do not think that that in any way affects the argument that the main alignment was the basis of such modifications.

We know that this great alignment passes through the camp at Alfoldean Bridge, and although it does not pass through Billingshurst it is within a hundred yards of it, and, as a matter of fact, is very much nearer the actual line of the road than Mr. Belloc's alignment from the same spot (Borough Hill, Pulborough) to Anstie Grange Farm, which (according to him) exactly coincides with it, and which he chose for that very (supposed) reason. There must have been some reason for this divergence of a hundred yards through what is now Billingshurst, but it is worthy of remark that the actual road rejoins the main alignment several miles before Alfoldean Bridge, and I am therefore of opinion that, up to this point, no modification of the main alignment was considered necessary. I have mentioned on a previous page (page 38) that a slight bend occurs at Alfoldean Bridge, and it is here, I believe, that the divergence towards Dorking Gap really began, because the camp at Dorking was now their objective, and a continuance towards London Bridge would have taken the road too far to the east. On the other hand, only a slight bend at this point was practicable, if the steep slopes of Leith Hill were to be avoided.

I should say that the course adopted would be this. Just as in the case of the Chichester–Pulborough alignment, this could be plotted with the greatest ease from the summit of the Downs at Gumber Corner, so from a point near the summit of Leith Hill, an alignment could be plotted from Alfoldean Camp to Dorking Camp, and incidentally to the crossing of the Mole at Burford Bridge, since Burford Bridge is exactly on that alignment.[1] Of course the road could not follow that alignment exactly, but I am strongly of opinion that in every case the direct alignment would be plotted out, whether it were practicable for the road to follow that line or not.

In this case Anstie Grange Farm, at a height of

[1] Owing to the sharp rise just north of Alfoldean Bridge the Camp itself is not visible from Leith Hill, so the sight would be taken onto the summit above the Camp.

about 450 feet, seems to have been the highest point to which the engineers found it practicable to carry the road, and from here it takes an almost straight line to the camp at Dorking. Why it did not go absolutely straight there is nothing to show, but, as a matter of fact, there is a slight bend just at Bentsbrook Farm. In view of the appreciable bend in the road which takes place at Alfoldean Bridge, I am of opinion that the foregoing hypothesis is the correct one ; but also, in view of the fact that the road at Billingshurst is not quite on that alignment, and that the 12 miles or so from Billingshurst to Anstie Grange Farm is almost dead straight, it may be that an alignment may have been run from Billingshurst to Anstie Grange Farm. Such an alignment would never be more than 25 or 30 yards off the road, but it would not quite coincide with it, nor would it pass through Alfoldean Bridge, but some 30 yards to the west of it.

But whichever alternative we adopt, it is, I think, beyond question, that both of them were based upon the great alignment from Pulborough to London which does pass exactly through Alfoldean Bridge.

If my hypothesis of the three great alignments forming a " closed traverse " be admitted, as I think it must be admitted by any practical engineer or topographical surveyor, the problem is solved so far as the general scheme of construction is concerned. And as regards the road itself, its course from Chichester, certainly as far as Burford Bridge, is perfectly well known and is not in dispute.

But it is from Burford Bridge onwards that the actual course of the Stane Street becomes a matter of controversy.

Subject to the correction of his defective topography and miscalculation of alignments, Mr. Belloc puts up a strong case for his theory that the Stane Street followed the course of the straight 2 miles A–B as far as Merton Abbey, and from there to London Bridge. But on page 277 he says:

" The whole of my argument is based upon the exact alignment of the Stane Street, where it has survived, with the direction of London Bridge, and upon the identity of the crossing of the Wandle with Merton Abbey."

On emerging from the Dorking Gap onto Juniper Hill the shortest way would, of course, be a direct line to London Bridge; and it is evident that Mr. Belloc was under the impression that the road A–B pointed to London Bridge, (he has drawn it so on his map) and that Merton Abbey was on that direct line. But, as a matter of fact, it isn't; and therefore the exactitude of the alignment on which the whole of his argument is based having proved imaginary, the whole of his argument falls to the ground. There remains the identity of the crossing of the Wandle with Merton Abbey. This identity may, I think, be regarded as established, but it is not on Mr. Belloc's alignment from Juniper Hill to London Bridge, but on the direct main alignment from Chichester.

It is, however, approximately on the line of A–B produced, and this fact that A–B produced points in the direction of Merton Abbey is the one and only thread on which hangs its claim to be regarded as part of the Stane Street at all.

If it pointed anywhere else (unless indeed it pointed to Ashtead or Epsom), even if it pointed to London Bridge, its claim would be a very slender one, since by pointing to London Bridge it would miss the Camp at Merton and the crossing of the Wandle by over $\frac{1}{4}$ mile.

One would have thought that when it was decided to abandon the direct line and adopt the divergent route via Pulborough, a direct line from Juniper Hill to London Bridge would have been taken after the passage of Dorking Gap, rather than joining the direct line from Chichester near Merton Abbey. Such a route would have been slightly shorter, and, so far as one can judge from the map, would have afforded an almost better crossing of the Wandle, passing through the middle of the deer park of Morden Hall, and well to the east of all complications of the Wandle river.

But there are two possible explanations of the course actually adopted. The first is that, very possibly, the first section of the road out of London to the crossing of the Wandle, may have been actually completed, or far advanced, before it was decided to abandon the direct line to Chichester, and therefore the road from Juniper Hill would make a slight deflection to join hands with the existing section at Merton. I have mentioned elsewhere that there are reasons (shared by other writers) for supposing that the Stane Street was built from London to Chichester, rather than from Chichester to London. This is one of them.

The other explanation is that, even in those early days, there may have been such a thing as red tape, and rigid adherence to established precedent, even if opposed to common sense. Now the fixed principle of construction of these Roman roads was, where a divergence became necessary, to return to the main alignment at the *earliest possible opportunity*. So that instead of driving straight on from Mickleham Downs to London Bridge, the road went slightly out of its way to comply with established precedent and joined the main alignment near Merton Abbey.

But, it may be objected, Merton Abbey is by no means the earliest possible opportunity for rejoining the main alignment ; this might have been done in the neighbourhood of Leatherhead, immediately after the crossing of the Mole at Burford Bridge. So it might ; and I shall now produce very strong presumptive evidence to show that this is what was done, and that, from the neighbourhood of Leatherhead, the Stane Street followed the direct line from Chichester through Epsom, Ewell, Morden and Merton Abbey, straight to Old London Bridge.

Nothing in the way of absolute proof is possible at present, but the coincidences of alignment which my exact investigations have brought to light are too remarkable to be ignored, and afford a reasonable hope that further archæological research along the track of those alignments may produce such proof. Even as it is, some slight confirmation is furnished by Mr. Belloc's footnote on page 277 :

" There have been certain finds within the neighbourhood of this line, and Roach Smith (*Journal of the Archæological Association*, vol. xxxii, p. 481) argues for it in Ewell Parish, *but not anywhere near the alignment I take*. It is of course evident that no indication not identical with the alignment is of service to my hypothesis."

Quite so. But in any case his hypothesis, as we have seen, does not rest upon a very sure foundation ; and if these indications are not anywhere near the alignment he takes, the inference would seem to be, not that the indications may be brushed aside and disregarded, but that, as in the case of the second limb, the alignment Mr. Belloc takes is wrong.

Now Mr. Belloc's hypothesis, as he himself admits, is founded solely upon a stretch of road 2 miles in length, and supposed to be Roman, which runs from the summit of Mickleham Downs at a height of 450 feet in the direction of Merton Abbey, and which for centuries has fallen out of use as a highway. Where last seen it curves round in the direction of Croydon, and no trace of a Roman road has been discovered between the termination of that road and Merton Abbey, a distance of about 9 miles.

But it will be remembered that Epsom is exactly on the main alignment from London Bridge to Chichester, and if we follow that alignment through the camp at Merton Abbey, and on through Morden, we come to a stretch of road, also 2 miles in length, and almost dead straight, which is *right on* that alignment.

For the first mile, from Stonecot Nursery to the Queen Victoria Inn, the road does not quite coincide with the alignment, Stonecot Nursery being some 30 yards off it, but for the second mile, from the Queen Victoria Inn to the corner of Nonsuch Park, the coincidence is *exact*. Both before and after this straight 2 miles the modern road winds a good deal, and there are a number of elbows in it, but the alignment cuts through these divergences from time to time so that, taken as a whole, and in view of the exact coincidence above mentioned, it may be said that the road from Epsom to London Bridge follows the main alignment.

Before going further let us compare the claims of these two stretches of road, each 2 miles long, to be regarded as belonging to Stane Street. In the first case we have a disused road leading to or from nowhere in particular, but pointing in a direction which will join one of the main alignments of Stane Street. This piece of road is marked "Ermyn Street" on the Ordnance map.

On the other hand we have a road which survives as a modern highway, and which, instead of pointing so as to *join* the main alignment some 9 miles further on, is *right on* that alignment, and is in exact alignment with the known section of the Stane Street between London Bridge and Merton Abbey. In the opposite direction it points exactly to Ewell and Epsom.

But this coincidence of alignment is not the only shot in my locker. If we follow it up still further, beyond Epsom, we come to the site of an old Roman Camp close to St. Giles Church, Ashtead. Mr. Belloc mentions this Camp, but since it is nearly a mile off his own pet alignment, he dismisses it as summarily as he did the two main alignments from London to Chichester, and London to Pulborough, and as he does the " finds " previously mentioned.

Now it so happens that this Roman Camp is also exactly on the main alignment from London to Chichester. When I say " exactly " on the alignment, I do not mean that the alignment passes right through the middle of this Camp as the alignments do through all the other Camps (except Dorking, where it passes through the N.W. corner). In this case, as a matter of fact, the alignment just misses the north western boundary of the Camp, or in other words, the Camp would be just on the south side of the road, and for this there appears to be a reasonable explanation.

This Camp is roughly one third of the way between those at Dorking and Merton, and the distance from either of these would be too short for a day's march. I am therefore of opinion that this was not one of the regular *Mansiones* of the Stane Street, but a depot of some sort, either for training purposes or for military stores (or possibly a sanatorium ; its proximity to the wells at Epsom might account for this). And in order that this depot should not be disturbed by the frequent passage of troops through it, it was placed at the side, instead of in the middle of the road. I think this, if anything, strengthens rather than weakens my argument that this was the course of the Stane Street.

I will now consider the point at which the road from Burford Bridge may have joined the main alignment.

After crossing Burford Bridge, the road is supposed to have crossed the lawn of Juniper Hall, where traces of it have been found. If this direction be followed up it will be found to lead a little east of the horse-shoe bend of the river Mole within which is situated a house called " The Priory." Whether this is on the site of one of those religious houses which are found in close proximity to Roman roads I do not know, but the name is suggestive. The line further continued joins the main alignment from Chichester to London at a point about a mile south-east of Leatherhead.

This I believe to have been the course taken by the Stane Street after crossing Burford Bridge, rather than that to Point A, and from there to Merton Abbey. The situation can be best understood by reference to the map (Fig 3, p. 43).

The advantages of my hypothesis as compared with Mr. Belloc's are as follows :

(1) It rejoins the main alignment at a very much earlier stage (10 miles), with no appreciable loss in point of distance.

(2) It avoids the steep climb up the spur of Juniper Hill, and the detour round the steep Combe just below point A, and a further steep climb up to Tyrrell's Wood.

(3) The highest point reached by this route is just over 300 feet as compared with 448 feet by the other.

(4) From Burford Bridge to the junction with the main alignment is a continuation of the alignment from Alfoldean Bridge, (Fig. 3, p. 43) subject to a slight divergence to avoid the spur of Juniper Hill, as the modern road does.

From Burford Bridge to point A is not on any recognisable alignment, and the gradient is increased rather than diminished.

Another consideration is the following :

All the way from Chichester to Burford Bridge, with the exception of a few short distances where it has disappeared, the Stane Street either survives as a modern highway, or its course can be identified. The last stage from Merton to London is no exception to this rule, and the nearer one gets to London the greater the probability, it seems to me, of the modern road following more or less closely the line of the Stane Street, since it is in close proximity to that line that centres of population might be expected to spring up. We find such centres of population in Epsom and Ewell, exactly on the main alignment, with 2 miles of the modern highway coinciding with that alignment, and the rest of the road conforming to it in its general direction and ultimate destination. We also have Leatherhead and Mickleham very close to that alignment.

But on Mr. Belloc's route along A–B we find nothing at all ; not a trace of any road, ancient or modern (other than cross roads) except this isolated 2 miles of abandoned road leading to or from nowhere and whose sole claim to consideration is the fact that it points towards Merton Abbey.

The case for my hypothesis is, I think, overwhelming.

There are two slight modifications of my hypothesis, arising out of another curious coincidence of alignment.

These modifications do not affect my main contention that the Stane Street joined the main alignment in the neighbourhood of Leatherhead, and passed via Epsom direct to London Bridge ; they only affect the exact spot at which the junction took place.

The coincidence of alignment is this :

In the horse-shoe bend of the river Mole containing " The Priory " referred to on a previous page, there are two bridges, one on the northern, the other on the southern side of the horse-shoe, affording communication between The Priory, and Leatherhead and Mickleham respectively, and a short cut between the two last named places.

Now the first of these bridges is precisely on the main alignment from Chichester to London Bridge. I am inclined to think that this is nothing but a coincidence, but on the other hand, it may be something more ; and I prefer to consider every possibility.

The first modification then, is that, after crossing Burford Bridge the Stane Street crossed over these two bridges, and joined the main alignment at the northernmost of the two (*see* map, Fig. 3, page 43).

The argument in favour of this is that the main alignment would have been reached ¾ mile sooner, and the road would have crossed the spur of Juniper Hill at a slightly lower level. Against it are two additional crossings of the river, and the fact that traces of the Stane Street are supposed to have been found on the lawn of Juniper Hall.

The second modification is this :

About a mile south of Dorking Camp the Stane Street has been identified at a spot close to Bentsbrook Farm (Fig. 2, page 33). Here there is a distinct bend, as of two alignments meeting ; the southern one coming from Anstie Grange Farm and the northern one pointing at Dorking Camp. Now if this alignment be continued through the middle of the Camp it will be found to just clear the sharp bend of the river Mole about ¾ mile north-west of Burford Bridge, at what is called " Ham Bank " (Fig. 3, page 43). This line would pass west of the river, so that instead of crossing at Burford Bridge the road would have joined the main alignment just west of Ham Bank, and crossed the river by the bridge on that alignment, the one on the north side of the horse-shoe, which, as already mentioned, is precisely on the main alignment.

Here there would only have been a single crossing of the river, and a still earlier junction with the main alignment (over a mile before the Horse-shoe Bridge), and a still lower level might have been maintained by a very slight divergence. The argument for this is much stronger than for the first modification, but I am inclined to discard the second also for the reason that the crossing of the Stane Street at Burford Bridge appears to have been established by the Archæologists.

Moreover, had the road followed this route, traces of it would almost certainly have been found (though possibly overlooked) in making the railway, since the southern end of Norbury tunnel is exactly on the alignment.

My final hypothesis therefore is as follows :

(1) That the Stane Street was planned on the basis of a preliminary survey comprising three great alignments, forming a " closed traverse " viz :

> London Bridge to Chichester.
> Chichester to Pulborough.
> Pulborough to London Bridge.

with possibly an intermediate alignment from London Bridge through Dorking Camp to the summit of the

South Downs at Gumber Corner; but this alignment was abandoned as a practicable route for the road.

(2) That from Pulborough Bridge to Billingshurst was merely a cutting of the Corner between the second and third great alignments.

(3) That from Billingshurst to Alfoldean Camp and Anstie Grange Farm was based directly on the third great alignment taken onto the sky-line of Brockham Warren.

(4) That the negotiation of Dorking Gap was based upon an alignment from Alfoldean Camp over the summit of Leith Hill to Dorking Camp and Burford Bridge and to its junction with the first great alignment east of Leatherhead.

(5) That from that point of junction the Stane Street coincided with the first great alignment all the way to its final destination at the southern end of Old London Bridge, passing by Ashtead Camp, through Epsom, Ewell, Morden, and the crossing of the Wandle near Merton Abbey.

(6) That the 2 miles of Roman road over Mickleham Downs A–B does not belong to the Stane Street at all, but, as an alternative, if it does so belong, that from point B near Thirty Acres Barn, the road inclined to the left and joined the main alignment between Ashtead and Epsom rather than at Merton Abbey.

So far as I can see, the only weak spot in my argument is the presence of that straight 2 miles of Roman road A–B, which it seems impossible to account for otherwise than as part of Stane Street, although, as I have shown, the topographical arguments are all against its being so.

But even if we suppose that the Roman engineers had some reason for taking the more difficult route up the steep slope of Juniper Hill, and accept A–B as belonging to Stane Street, that still leaves unaccounted for the bend near Thirty Acres Barn, and the fact that the road has been traced nearly to the Grand Stand on Epsom racecourse. Mr. Belloc himself makes no attempt to explain it; nor does he suggest that it was from there that the road went to Merton Abbey; he claims that it went straight on from point B. But if that were so there must surely be some trace of it under conditions where the bend itself has survived so unmistakably, but no such trace is to be found, and I am therefore forced to the conclusion that the direction of this bend is the one and only course of this piece of Roman road.

Its appearance on the map (Fig. 4, page 51) gives no indication of any intention to join the main alignment in the neighbourhood of Epsom, or even at Merton Abbey, and by the time the Grand Stand is reached the probability of such intention has practically vanished. Such a junction would involve a bend approaching a right angle, a thing unheard of in a Roman road.

We are faced then with the following alternative. If we accept A–B as the Stane Street, we must reject the whole 16 miles from London Bridge to Ashtead, which exactly coincides with the direct alignment to Chichester, and all the positive marks of identification which have been found along that route. In addition to those already mentioned there is a great deal of evidence to show that Ewell was a place of considerable importance during the Roman occupation of Britain, and that the road almost certainly passed through it, and probably through Epsom as well, and the fact of Ashtead Camp being on the main alignment makes me very unwilling to exclude it from the scheme of the road. But if we accept the Chichester alignment we must reject A–B and its continuation towards Croydon, for to reconcile the two seems to me impossible ; and approaching the problem, as I do, with a mind unbiassed by any previous knowledge or study of the subject, the weight of evidence in favour of the Chichester alignment appears overwhelming.

But there must be some explanation of this isolated and abandoned stretch of road A–B, and the first point that strikes me is, why is it called " Ermyn Street " on the Ordnance maps ? Archæological research does not come within the scope of the present little work, and it is with the utmost diffidence that I venture to put forward the following conjecture.

Reference has been made on a previous page to an old ferry some 300 yards east of Old London Bridge which, it has been suggested, was the crossing place of the Stane Street. Now the line of " Ermine Street " coming from the north strikes the Thames at a point which must have been very close to this ferry, and it seems possible that Ermine Street may have been continued across the river from this point, perhaps via Streatham and Carshalton, to effect a junction with the old Pilgrims Way from Winchester to Canterbury which crossed the Mole a little south of Burford Bridge.

This continuation of Ermyn Street, being superseded by the Stane Street at a later date, would fall out of use, but the crossing of the Mole at Burford Bridge being common to both, and the traces of the road over Mickleham Downs being so conspicuous, the assumption that this was the Stane Street is the obvious and natural one, so obvious in fact that the possibility of error in this matter, or of an alternative explanation of this isolated stretch of Roman road, does not seem to have occurred to anyone. This may be attributed in part to the well-known tendency of errors in textbooks to be quoted and perpetuated by subsequent writers, and in part to lack of expert knowledge in topographical surveying, a subject but little understood except by those whose business it is.

That there must be an alternative explanation, which I would commend to the attention of Archæologists, I feel firmly convinced, and the very remarkable coincidences of alignment disclosed by my exact investigations encourage the hope that such explanation may, some day, be forthcoming, and that the course of what is, perhaps, the most interesting of all the Roman roads in Britain, may be established with some degree of certainty.

# Appendix A

## ERRORS DUE TO CARELESSNESS OR PRINTER'S ERRORS

p. 22, footnote.   *For* 2 in. *read* $\frac{1}{2}$ in.

p. 52, footnote.   *For* Tyrell's Court *read* Tyrell's Wood.

p. 59, diagram.   Fig. 3.   *For* 4th Limb 26° 30' E. of N *read* 28° 54' E. of N.

p. 60, line 2.   *For* 6$\frac{3}{4}$ *read* 5$\frac{3}{4}$.

p. 60, line 11.   *For* under 28° 15' *read* 28° 54'.

p. 87, line 7.   *For* Westward *read* Eastward.

p. 91, line 8.   *For* 3 *read* 4.

p. 91, line 15.   *For* 400 *read* 300.

p. 92, line 1.   *For* no more than 665 *read* just over 700.

p. 92, diagram, Fig. 7.   Incorrectly Drawn.   The Stane Street crosses the Downs at 700 not 600 feet.

p. 97, line 26.   *For* 3$\frac{3}{4}$ *read* 2$\frac{3}{4}$.

p. 97, line 27.   *For* 3$\frac{3}{4}$ *read* 2$\frac{3}{4}$.

p. 98, line 9.   *For* 3$\frac{3}{4}$ *read* 2$\frac{3}{4}$.

p. 100, line 7.   *For* Northward by a little West *read* West by a little North.

p. 101, line 11.   *For* Brackham *read* Brockham.

p. 102, line 18.   *For* which *read* what.

p. 195, line 24.   *For* The height of the South Downs *read* Borough Hill.

p. 214, line 11.   *For* to the left *read* straight on.

p. 219, line 23.   *For* Wareham *read* Warehead.

p. 235, line 25.   *For* left *read* right.

p. 245, line 3.   *For* 3$\frac{3}{4}$ read 2$\frac{3}{4}$.

p. 245, line 15.   *For* 3$\frac{3}{4}$ *read* 2$\frac{3}{4}$.

p. 249, line 22.   *For* East *read* West.

p. 259, line 21.   *For* North and a little East *read* West and
   a little North.

p. 226, line 10.   *For* below *read* above.

*Folding map*.   *For* 3rd Alignment 28° 54′ E. of N. *read*
                4th Alignment 28° 54′ E. of N.

The highest contour on Box Hill should read 700 instead of 200.

The height at Gumber Corner is 700 not 600 feet.

# Appendix B

## ERRORS DUE TO MISCALCULATION AND MIS-STATEMENTS ARISING THEREFROM

p. 50, line 5.   *For* exact *read* approximate.

p. 50, line 7.   *For* 55 miles and 3 furlongs *read* 55·1410 miles.

p 51, line 27.   *For* London Bridge *read* Merton Abbey.

p. 52, footnote.   *For* 3 in 309·76 *read* 3 in 330·15.

p. 52, footnote, line 3.   *For* exact *read* approximate.

line 4.   *For* London Bridge *read* Merton Abbey.

p. 58, line 3.   *For* 55 miles and 3 furlongs *read* 55·1410 miles.

p. 58, line 16.   *For* 30° 25′ *read* 32° 46′ 30″·44.

p. 58, line 20.   *For* 52° 45′ *read* 53° 54′ 15″·60.

p. 58, line 22.   *For* 22° 30′ *read* 24° 39′.

p. 59, diagram Fig. 3.

*For* 30° 25′ *read* 32° 46′ 30″·44.

*For* 37° 15′ N. of E. *read* 53° 54′ 15″·60.

*For* 22° 30′ *read* 24° 39′.

*For* 7° 30′ *read* 6° 34′.

*For* 26° 30′ *read* 30° 42′ 15″·7.

p. 60, line 10.   *For* straight *read* approximately.

p. 60, line 10.   *For* London Bridge *read* Merton Abbey.

p. 60, line 11.   *For* 28° 15′ *read* 30° 42′ 15″·7.

p. 60, line 14.   *For* at the foot of the Bridge *read* Near Merton Abbey.

p. 63, line 7.   *For* London Bridge *read* Merton Abbey.

p. 69, line 3.   *For* Pulborough Bridge *read* Hardham Camp.

p. 70, line 18.   *For* London Bridge *read* Merton Abbey.

p. 98, line 7.   *For* Todhurst Farm *read* Billingshurst.

p. 98, line 6.   *For* absolutely *read* nearly.

p. 98, line 7.   *For* The Shoulder of Leith Hill *read* Anstie Grange Farm.

p. 98, line 8. *For* 7° *read* 8° 12′ 31″.

p. 98, line 10. *For* 29° 20′ *read* 32° 55′ 44″.

p. 102, line 25. *For* London Bridge *read* Merton Abbey.

p. 106, line 16. *For* do not coincide until, etc. *read* do not coincide at all.

p. 106, line 20. *For* exactly coincides *read* does not coincide.

p. 107, Diagram Fig. 11. Correctly drawn, but incompatible with an alignment to London Bridge.

p. 108. *After* I have concluded *add* wrongly.

p. 111, line 20. The supposed line is on London Bridge and Merton Abbey is over $\frac{1}{4}$ mile off that line.

p. 112, fig. 12. The scale of heights is multiplied by about 35, not by 50 as stated.

p. 112, line 11. *For* London Bridge *read* Merton Abbey.

p. 112, line 14. *For* Pulborough Bridge *read* Hardham Camp.

p. 119, line 23. The point referred to is 200 yards off the alignment.

p. 113, line 20–22 ⎱ These two statements are incompatible. If the alignment points to London Bridge it cannot point to Merton Abbey and *vice versa*.
p. 134, line 6 ⎰

p. 136, line 6. *For* accurately to *read* 5 furlongs west of.

p. 137, fig. 14. Incorrectly drawn. The alignment passes West of Morden Hall, not as shown.

p. 152, line 1. The measurements in question are wrong.

p. 103, fig. 17. The alignment shown here is not the same as that from Todhurst Farm to Anstie Grange Farm.

p. 197, fig. 18. Incorrectly drawn. The alignments meet at Anstie Grange Farm ; not as shown. Folly Farm is on the 400 foot contour $\frac{1}{2}$ mile further North.

p. 203, line 24. Such a line is not on the alignment A–B produced.

p. 205, fig. 19. The alignment shown here which is supposed to be from Juniper Hill is in fact on the direct line from Chichester.

p. 213, line 8. *For* 37$\frac{1}{4}$° N. of E. *read* 53° 54′ 15″·6.

p. 213, line 9. *For* direction *read* mean direction.

p. 213, line 20. *For* exactly *read* approximately.

or *For* Pulborough Bridge *read* Hardham Camp.

p. 228, line 18. *For* exactly *read* approximately.

       or *For* Pulborough Bridge *read* Hardham Camp.

p. 241, line 5. Pulborough Bridge is over 100 yards out of the alignment.

p. 242, line 3. *For* exactly *read* approximately.

     line 5. *For* Pulborough Bridge *read* Hardham Camp.

     line 18. The alignment does not pass through this point at all.

p. 244, line 15. *For* 37¼° North of East *read* 53° 54′ 15″·6.

     line 19. *For* 59° North of East *read* 32° 55′ 44″.

     line 20. *For* 22° *read* 21°.

p. 245, line 2. *For* 59° N. of E. *read* 32° 55′ 44″.

p. 252, line 2. *For* are the continuation of *read* converge on.

p. 252, line 24. The alignment between Park Street and Rowhook is over 150 yards from the Borough Hill— Leith Hill alignment.

p. 259, line 26. The alignments do not meet at this point but at Anstie Grange Farm.

p. 260, line 3–5. The alignment does not pass through either Alfoldean or Ockley.

p. 261, line 13–14. This point is described on p. 100 as that where the two alignments meet.

p. 263, fig. 20. The alignments shown as meeting at Anstie Grange Farm are described on p. 100 as meeting elsewhere.

p. 269, line 16–18. This statement has no foundation in fact.

p. 274, line 12. *For* under *read* over.

p. 274, line 14. *For* points *read* does not point.

p. 276, line 20. A straight alignment from here cannot pass through both places.

p. 277, line 16. The argument is based upon a fallacy.

p. 278, line 16–17. *For* in question *read* from Chichester to London Bridge.

p. 279, line 9–10. The straight 2 miles between Ewell and Morden Hall exactly coincides with the alignment from Chichester to London Bridge.

p. 280, line 7. The coincidence of alignment from Chichester is a strong piece of evidence which has been overlooked.

p. 281, line 10      } These statements are based upon a fallacy.

     line 13–14 }

p. 282, line 9.   The alignment on Epsom Downs is not coinci-
dent with that line.

p. 283, line 10.   There is no such coincidence.

line 19.   *For* at *read* 5 furlongs west of.

p. 284, line 5.   It is only unswerving as far as Merton Abbey.

p. 286, line 3.   *For* does *read* does not.

line 15.   *For* precisely at *read* 60 yards west of.

line 21–22.   The alignment is not recovered again.

line 26.   *After* bridge *add* but not on the same alignment.

line 27.   The line further prolonged points 5 furlongs
west of London Bridge and does not pass through
any of the points mentioned.

p. 287, line 13.   There is no exactitude and no coincidence.

*Folding Map.*

  *For* 30° 25′ E. of N. *read* 32° 46′ 30″·44.

  *For* 37° 15′, N. of E. *read* 53° 54′ 15″·60.

  *For* 29° 30′ E. of N. *read* 32° 55′ 44″.

  *For* 22° 30′ E. of N. *read* 24° 39′.

  *For* 7° 30′ E. of N. *read* 6° 34′.

  For 3rd alignment 28° 54′ E. of N. *read* 4th alignment
30° 42′ 15″·7.

Taking Chichester as the starting point, London Bridge is
2¼ miles N.W. of its true position, and other places in similar
proportion (approximately).

The site of Merton Abbey, and the whole 7 miles or more
from there to London Bridge, have been moved from their
proper position onto Mr. Belloc's imaginary alignment from
Juniper Hill to London Bridge, and the 2 miles of road over
Mickleham Downs has been drawn pointing to London Bridge
instead of to Merton Abbey.

# Appendix C

## GEOGRAPHICAL CO-ORDINATES FOR COMPUTING ALIGNMENTS

| Place | Latitude North | | | Longitude West | | |
|---|---|---|---|---|---|---|
| | ° | ′ | ″ | ° | ′ | ″ |
| Chichester East Gate . . . | 50 | 50 | 07·83 | 0 | 46 | 21·22 |
| Gumber Corner . . . . . | 50 | 54 | 25·10 | 0 | 37 | 06·16 |
| Hardham Camp . . . . . | 50 | 56 | 46·10 | 0 | 31 | 57·60 |
| Pulborough Bridge * . . . | 50 | 57 | 20·10 | 0 | 30 | 38·10 |
| Borough Hill, Pulborough . | 50 | 57 | 48·60 | 0 | 29 | 42·40 |
| Todhurst Farm . . . . . | 50 | 59 | 20·60 | 0 | 28 | 34·50 |
| Billingshurst . . . . . | 51 | 01 | 20·06 | 0 | 27 | 0·68 |
| Alfoldean Bridge (Camp) . . | 51 | 05 | 08·16 | 0 | 24 | 13·80 |
| Ockley . . . . . . . | 51 | 08 | 45·30 | 0 | 21 | 39·70 |
| Terminal D (Leith Hill) . . | 51 | 10 | 45·70 | 0 | 20 | 04·84 |
| Mark X (Leith Hill) . . . | 51 | 10 | 51·50 | 0 | 20 | 17·00 |
| Anstie Grange Farm . . . | 51 | 11 | 03·38 | 0 | 20 | 02·46 |
| Anstiebury Camp . . . . | 51 | 11 | 0·00 | 0 | 21 | 0·00 |
| Dorking Camp . . . . . | 51 | 13 | 49·30 | 0 | 19 | 54·60 |
| Burford Bridge . . . . . | 51 | 15 | 12·02 | 0 | 19 | 16·75 |
| Point A ⎫ (Roman Road) . . | 51 | 16 | 22·10 | 0 | 18 | 26·60 |
| Point B ⎭ | 51 | 17 | 43·10 | 0 | 17 | 15·00 |
| Point C, Juniper Hill . . . | 51 | 15 | 46·45 | 0 | 19 | 09·65 |
| Ashtead Camp . . . . . | 51 | 18 | 31·00 | 0 | 17 | 24·00 |
| Nonsuch Park (S.W. Corner) | 51 | 21 | 30·00 | 0 | 14 | 20·80 |
| Merton Abbey (Site of) . . | 51 | 24 | 48·00 | 0 | 10 | 55·75 |
| Wandle Bridge . . . . . | 51 | 24 | 58·00 | 0 | 10 | 44·50 |
| Old London Bridge * . . | 51 | 30 | 22·20 | 0 | 05 | 08·65 |

* Southern end.

# INDEX

A—B, Roman Road, 50, 55, 62, 72, 78, 81, 82, 83

Abinger, 18

Alfoldean Bridge, 14, 38, 40, 69–71, 78

Alfoldean Camp, 14, 40, 68, 70, 81

Alignments, coincidences of, 18, 67, 74–5, 78–9; computation of, 19; curvature of, 20; passing through camps, 67–68; modifications of, 69, 70

Anstiebury Camp, 34, 37, 44

Anstie Grange Farm, 14, 37–39, 41, 42, 44, 50, 70, 71, 79, 81

Appledram, 26

Arun River, 28; crossing of, 14, 23, 27, 38, 68, 69

Ashtead Camp, 76, 81, 82

Azimuth, definition of, 21

Bearing, definition of, 21

Belloc, Mr., his alignments, 16–64, 66, 69, 72; alleged coincidences of, 26, 34, 50, 52–54; errors of, 23–29, 31–40, 42–44, 48, 52–59; plotting of, 18, 20; his basis of argument, 72; fabrication of maps, 10, 56, 58, 62, 63, 72; fact and fiction, 26; carelessness, 10, 32, 36, 37, 48, 56, Appendix A; closing error of traverse,

62; inaccuracy, 10, 19, 20, 26, 32, 42–44, 50, 52, 56, 57, Appendix B; figures, how arrived at, 19–20; insistence on exactitude, 19, 23, 24, 26, 27, 31, 32, 35, 38, 39, 42, 48, 50, 52–54, 57, 63, 72; jumping to conclusions, 24, 38, 52, 72; method of computation, 21, 34, 59, 61; of procedure, 65; terminal points, 17, 34–37, 49, 50, 65; topography, 11, 15, 22, 34, 38, 52–63, 71

Bencomb, 52

Bentsbrook Farm, 71, 79

Billingshurst, 14, 38, 39, 69, 70, 71, 81

Borough Hill, 34, 38, 39, 40, 68

Box Hill, 36, 66

Brockham Warren, 26, 35, 39, 45, 49, 69, 81

Burford Bridge, 14, 41, 45, 48, 50, 70, 74, 77, 78, 80, 81, 83

Camps, 12, 76; selection of sites for, 18, 69

Canterbury, 83

Carshalton, 83

Chichester (East Gate), 12–15, 17, 62, 66, 68, 72–79, 82

Clapham Road, 63

Controversy, subject of, 15, 71

*Printed in Great Britain by* Butler & Tanner, *Frome and London*